And God Created Manyberries

And God Created Manyberries

Ron Wood

Frontenac House

Book and cover design: Epix Design
Cover image: Vance Rodewalt
Author photo: Michael R. Wood

Library and Archives Canada Cataloguing in Publication

Wood, Ron, 1942-
And God created Manyberries / Ron Wood.

ISBN 978-1-897181-15-7

1. Manyberries (Alta.)--Anecdotes. 2. Manyberries (Alta.)--Humor.
3. Canada--Politics and government--2006- --Humor. 4. Canadian wit and humor (English) I. Title.

FC3661.3.W65 2007 971.23'4 C2007-905265-7

We acknowledge the support of the Canada Council for the Arts for our publishing program. We also acknowledge the support of The Alberta Foundation for the Arts.

Canada Council   Conseil des Arts
for the Arts   du Canada

Printed and bound in Canada
Published by Frontenac House Ltd.
1138 Frontenac Avenue S.W.
Calgary, Alberta, T2T 1B6, Canada
Tel: 403-245-2491 Fax: 403-245-2380
editor@frontenachouse.com   www.frontenachouse.com

Contents

Disclaimer

The incidents, characters, locations, prices, geographic anomalies, dogs, cats, paint colours, vehicles, physical attributes, personal grooming habits, wardrobes and beverage consumption preferences in this book are all more or less coincidentally linked to persons who may still be living. And if not, certainly to individuals who have passed over the great divide and therefore are not in a position to sue for libel, slander, smear or loss of reputation.

The author's philosophy, if such exists, was shaped by a boyhood in Calgary followed by another boyhood in Ottawa where he followed various pursuits as a member of the Parliamentary Press Gallery, television anchorman and federal communications bureaucrat.

In his third boyhood he returned to Calgary to work as News Director for CKXL and CHFM Radio and won several regional and national radio awards, including the prestigious National Radio Award for Best Opinion/Commentary Broadcaster in 1989.

In his fourth, in 1990, he hired on as Press Secretary to Preston Manning, Leader of the Reform Party of Canada, and began a period of intense travel and commuting between Calgary and the nether regions of Canada, including Ottawa.

Even as the years advanced cruelly and inexorably, he entered a fifth house of boyhood when he signed on as EA/Communications Advisor to Official Opposition Leader John Reynolds. He followed Reynolds to the office of Opposition House Leader in the same capacity when Stephen Harper was elected Leader of the Opposition. He spent the following years working with the National Co-Chair of the Alliance and Conservative election campaigns and in the communications office of Opposition Leader Stephen Harper.

When he and Reynolds decided jointly to retire, the author told friends he had so much Ottawa that had to be scraped from his brain that the only possible location for the operation was Manyberries, Alberta. He flew home just days prior to the 2006 general election, voted, and disappeared somewhere on the vast prairie, or what's left of it in Alberta.

All of the characters' names in this friendly little book, which it is hoped will become an international best seller, are real names plucked from the annals of history and if not from there, transcribed from the walls of the Ranchmen's Inn in Manyberries, Alberta.

Unlike the actual creatures themselves, the names of some of the dogs have been altered to protect the innocent. Most of the cats' names are real, even those cats who should have been altered.

The author assumes no responsibility whatsoever for anything and has spent a lifetime practising and perfecting that assumption.

And God Created Manyberries

Foreward
– The Birth of Manyberries

You'd like Manyberries if you ever came to visit. You might even fall in love with the place and decide to spend the rest of your life here. Nobody would ever address you as stranger because there are no strangers allowed in Manyberries. That is to say that people here are so friendly they see you as a potential friend the first time they meet you.

One of the first people you might meet if you come any time of the year other than hunting season would be Perley. He's our Postmaster Sort-Of and Postal Delivery Man Sort-Of and as such is the only breathing federal government presence we have in Manyberries.

People here think that's about all the federal government should do: deliver the mail. We also think the federal government should raise and equip an army and do a few other things but not a lot of other things.

Some of those other things include being there for farmers when the weather conspires against them and their crops. In times like that we believe federal financial assistance should equal what farmers would be paid per bushel if there were worldwide grain shortages and prices were at historic highs.

Given that we believe in equal opportunity we also support financial assistance for ranchers when beef prices plummet due to oversupply or when other unforeseen problems like the mad cow crisis arise. In situations like this we believe federal assistance should be equal to the prices the ranchers would get if there were a worldwide beef shortage and prices were at historic highs.

A majority of Manyberrians also believe that the federal

government should step in when crude oil and natural gas prices soften to cover the difference between these lower prices and what the industry is paid in times of world crisis or undersupply.

There are others, those who drive, which is pretty near everybody 14 years and older, who think Ottawa should subsidize fuel prices at the pumps so nobody has to pay more than 40 cents a litre.

One thing we all agree on is that taxes are too high and the federal government should stop funding and subsidizing special interest groups. In the words of Purvis, another prominent Manyberries citizen, "They're paying painters to paint and poets to write poems and dancers to dance when all that money would be better spent buying us a water sprinkling truck to keep the dust down in summer." Folks in Manyberries like to keep things simple.

If you drop in at the Ranchmen's Saloon on a busy night you'll probably meet just about everybody who lives in Manyberries. You might have to hang around for a while to meet them all because the Ranchmen's Saloon can't accommodate 100 people all at once and that's roughly the population of our busy little metropolis. The proper name of the Ranchmen's, incidentally, is the Southern Ranchmen's Inn, which is appropriate because you can't get much more southern than Manyberries.

The head count of 100 doesn't include dogs, not even Three-Eyed Tom, the biggest dog in the world, who lives with Purvis. If you belly up to the bar at the Ranchmen's and something as big as a Shetland pony is sleeping by the front door, that will be Three-Eyed Tom. Three-Eyed Tom is called Three-Eyed because he has a spot between his eyes that appears to be a third eye. And of course once you get inside you'll meet Hazel, who waitresses the whole shebang. If you see two circular discs shining over in a dark corner, that will be Four-Eyed Tom, no relation to Three-Eyed, because Four-Eyed is human and wears spectacles so thick that he appears to have four eyes. At least that's what some of the folks claim.

If there's a Weimaraner sleeping outside the front door of the Ranchmen's, you'll find me inside and please do come over and say hello. We'll find you a chair and you can sit and chat with me and Purvis, Perley, Harry Charles (our Manyberries political analyst and all-round pundit), and whoever else is there.

Now that you're interested in visiting Manyberries, and perhaps staying here for life, you should know how to get here.

If you were to come from the east on one of those Toronto adventure tours, you'll probably arrive in a canoe via Manyberries Creek. A lot of people in Toronto think we travel by canoe or covered wagon out here. You'll have a lot of portaging to do because the creek isn't deep enough in most places to float a corked beer bottle. Try to come in the spring when the melt is on, especially if we had a lot of snow the previous winter, and you'll float the whole way because the creek will be up over its banks.

Once you reach latitude 49:20:17N and longitude 110:43:03W, haul the canoe out and look north. That bunch of buildings across the long-gone railroad tracks will be Manyberries. Leave the canoe and stroll over to the Ranchmen's and have a beer or something.

If your Toronto travel agent arranges an adventure tour in a covered wagon from the opposite direction, watch for a strange geographic anomaly in the form of a series of hills rising straight up out of the prairie. These will be the Cypress Hills; once you get to the western edge, gaze off into the southwest. You won't be able to see Manyberries from there but you will be looking in the right direction. Turn your ox team south and work your way down the southern slope. When you hit bottom, head southwest and by and by, if you're lucky, you'll come across Manyberries and if not, at least meet somebody who can tell you how to get here from wherever you are.

If you happen to come across an elderly couple sitting stark naked on lawn chairs on a sand dune, that will be Old Rutherford and the Mrs. This means you are getting closer to Manyberries and that you have discovered an area that is very important to some of the people who live here, especially those of us who hunt, because a lot of antelope can be found in this area. Not as many as there were before Old Rutherford and the Mrs discovered it and claimed it as their own personal beach without water, but there are still a few, and more drift back in October when it gets a little chilly for the Rutherfords to gather sunshine (as they call it). October is also when Old Rutherford has to be close to home to harvest his turnips and other root vegetables, so he and the Mrs do their sunshine gathering in their backyard with sheets of plywood covered in tinfoil for reflection and windbreaks against the cooler autumn breezes.

If you come by motor vehicle, and that's how most of us in the west travel these days, follow what is called the Red Coat Trail, named after the Royal Canadian Mounted Police who were once called the North West Mounted Police, or Red Coats. They are called Mounties today or worse by people they've stopped for speeding.

You might be wondering about the birth of Manyberries and how it was created and something of its history. It's a little known story but a very colourful one that more or less mirrors the history and development of humankind.

Many years ago, God was sitting at His Cabinet table with His whole Angelic Cabinet discussing some possibilities for the new world He was fashioning. On the table in front of each attendee there was a bowl of small bluish-black berries that they were all sampling and enjoying.

"What do you call these?" God asked the Agricultural Cabinet Angel.

"We don't name things anymore since You decided You had to name everything we create."

"Right, I forgot," God said, "but it's getting to the point where I simply can't do everything, so Secretary Angel, please make a note that I'm designating each of the Cabinet Angels as my official thing namers on anything we create that weighs less than 12 pounds." His decision was duly noted and he sampled another handful of the newly created berries.

"Boy, these things are so good they make music in your mouth," He observed. "We should call them musicberries."

"Well, we were thinking of making them available in a very limited region somebody will eventually call Saskatchewan and Alberta," the Cabinet Angel For Choosing Places told him.

"Saskaltamusicberries is a bit much of a name," God observed.

After a while, still thinking of the little berries as musical in taste, God decided on a name.

"Let there be Saskatunes," He said so excitedly that several of His Cabinet Angels got sore necks when they snapped awake.

The Cabinet Angel for Choosing Places looked down and groaned. "Aw Geez," he said, "You've gone and stuck a city in the middle of what won't be Saskatchewan for eons to come."

"What does Saskatchewan mean?" God asked.

"I don't know yet and we won't know for a long time because we still have to create some people to live there who'll come up with their own language."

God pointed down and lightning flew from His extended right forefinger. "Okay, so that's Saskatune gone and nobody will be any the wiser whenever they get around to naming it. But those berries are so damn good, we've gotta come up with a name for them."

"Sir," the Cabinet Angel Secretary interrupted, "You just made it official that You won't be involved in naming anything that weighs less than 12 pounds."

"Cripes, I'm just so damn hasty at times," God sighed. "Well, I won't over-ride Myself again, so I'll leave the naming to somebody else. But I can make another decision and I want this recorded, Cabinet Angel Secretary."

God paused for dramatic effect and looked around at His mostly

And God Created Manyberries

dozing Cabinet Angels. He thought and smiled into the future, knowing that when they got around to creating Canada, He was also going to create a democratic situation where the tiny people who thought they were Him on earth would be surrounded by tiny dozing cabinet ministers who would think of themselves as Cabinet Angels.

"I WANT THERE TO BE MANY BERRIES," He thundered.

Instantly, a very old brave named Many Berries found himself sitting somewhere in Saskatchewan, eating small berries and enjoying them immensely.

"Strange," the old brave thought, "here I am sitting and eating Saskatunes and it'll be millions of years before my people will even start to migrate in this direction. And probably thousands of years after that before they name these things Saskatunes."

He immediately went to a nearby rock and began scratching his name on it using a piece of broken sharp stone as a writing instrument. "When they do get here," he thought to himself, "if I'm on vacation or something, they won't be able to live here because this will prove I was here first and it'll be legal proof that I have already laid claim to this land."

"Aw God," said the Angel, "now You've gone and created a person named Many Berries and he's gone and named the damn berries Saskatunes."

"Well, I'm trying to govern this whole creating thing to the best of My abilities," God sort of moaned. He sat and pondered.

"I can't zap the old guy," He said. "It wouldn't be fair to zap him now that he's sitting there and enjoying the berries. We'll leave him alone and when we get around to creating Canada, we'll make sure that lawyers, when the Other Guy creates them, will have plenty of work for all of their professional lives."

"But You did intend that there be many berries, did You not?" The Cabinet Angel for Agriculture was a rural Angel and could be relied on to get the discussion back to the topic.

"Yeah I did," God said. "Cabinet Angel Secretary, read back exactly what I said."

"Well, actually You thundered it, God. You thundered, and I quote, 'I WANT THERE TO BE MANY BERRIES,' unquote."

God closed his eyes and imagined a place on earth where there would be all the berries anyone could ever eat. "I really do want there to be many berries for all the folks when they leave the Garden," He said quietly and somewhat plaintively.

Instantly, at a place in what would come to be known as Alberta, a small town appeared.

"Aw God," said the Cabinet Angel for Choosing Places, "now You've gone and created a town called Many Berries in a place where even gophers will have a hard time surviving."

"Well, I can remedy that," God said and pointed His forefinger down at the little town. Lightning flew from His finger tip. He hadn't spent much time in what would become southern Alberta and didn't take into account wind velocity so His trajectory was off by several degrees.

By the time the lightning exited His finger tip, most of the Cabinet Angels were packing their brief cases and getting ready to rush the door to make the noon opening at the bar and so didn't realize God had wrought only partial destruction of His unintentional creation. And God Himself never ever looked back at anything He destroyed.

Well, that's the true story as we understand it and it is said it was an old, very old, aboriginal Canadian who first told it to an equally old Hutterite elder who passed it on to several others, including Harry Charles, who passed it on to me.

So, if you're ever in southern Alberta and you come across a road sign that says Manyberries, you'll want to visit the place. Arrange to spend a few days there exploring the town, which shouldn't take more than 10 minutes, leaving you plenty of time for rest and relaxation at the Ranchmen's saloon. Most of the town that's still standing was the mistake God made and the charred area over on the east side is evidence of His effort to correct that mistake. Well, that's what we tell visitors every couple of years when Purvis burns his autumn trash and yard rakings and accidentally starts a small prairie fire.

Your few days here will also give you time to explore the countryside. And if while you are exploring you discover any berries, would you please drop into the Ranchmen's and tell us where they are?

Manyberries' Dominion Day

A bunch of us were sitting in the Ranchmen's a while back when the subject of Dominion Day found its way on to the agenda.

Over in Ottawa they insist on calling our July 1st national birthday Canada Day but here in Manyberries we call it Dominion Day, which is what our grandparents called it. If you have young grandparents, it's quite possible their grandparents called it Dominion Day too.

The Dominion Day versus Canada Day complaints occupied a large part of the remainder of the evening but we were still able to squeeze in a consensus at the end that it was time Manyberries had a parade of its own on July 1st.

Perley, our Postmaster Sort-Of and Postman Sort-Of, as a volunteer employee of the Post Office and therefore the only federal face we have in Manyberries, volunteered to act as parade organizer. He said he would survey the town folk and farmers and ranchers for miles around to see who would like to be in the parade.

Perley gets a pension cheque so he can afford to work for the Post Office for no remuneration. What he does as Postmaster Sort-Of is open mailboxes for people and scan their mail for NDP literature from Ottawa or Edmonton. If he finds any he takes it home to burn in his trash bin. As Postman Sort-Of, he delivers all the mail that's left to the houses in town. People gave him their mailbox keys some time back when he went to the mailbox building and found the floor littered with political pamphlets. He said you just couldn't leave stuff like that where children might find it. So he got the job and the people whose mail he delivers often invite him in for a drink when he makes his rounds. After heavy mail days, I've seen Perley walk into the Ranchmen's on his knees for his regular nightcap.

Actually, the better part of Perley's survey work was already done because most of the town's adult population was at the Ranchmen's that night and had agreed to participate in the parade. When Perley presented his report, that he was very encouraged about the potential for the parade, he got a resounding response from the regulars at the Ranchmen's. His ulterior motive for driving all over the country talking to farmers and ranchers was to scout for pheasants, partridge and grouse, but no one seemed to question him about that.

Perley is such an enthusiastic hunter that people know from September to early December he won't be delivering their mail because he has other priorities.

Purvis, who owns Three-Eyed Tom the giant dog, said he wanted to see a truck with all the town's dogs on it as one of the floats. Purvis enjoys being the owner of a dog that towers over every other dog in town and for miles around. This way everybody would see Three-Eyed Tom and all the other dogs together and have to acknowledge (again, for the umpteenth time) that Tom is indeed the biggest.

Three-Eyed is unlike other dogs in that he will not relieve himself on anything but motor vehicles. People say that Three-Eyed watches in particular for vehicles with U.S. licence plates so he can make his mark and put the fear of giant dogs into those that live south of the big border. Nobody objected to the suggestion and Four-Eyed Tom volunteered his flatbed and said he'd drive the dog float.

Apart from Purvis, Four-Eyed Tom is about the only human Three-Eyed Tom seems to genuinely like.

Perley said he'd put his old Pontiac station wagon in the parade as the official representative vehicle of the federal government. He would unscrew the federal sign from the Post Office mailbox building and hang it with wires on one side of the vehicle. He would have to make two rounds so the people watching it on both sides of the street would be able to see the sign. "It's bilingual," he said, "and that'll make it a sort of national unity float."

Hazel at the bar said she'd toss a couple of empty kegs in the back of her pickup and that would be the official float of the Ranchmen's. Somebody suggested she also put tubs full of iced beer in the back and hand out bottles just like they hand out candy in some big city parades. Hazel drew the line at that but said she might hand out 10-percent-off coupons.

Harry Charles said he'd put his Renault station wagon in the parade. With its air conditioning and leather seats, not to mention its unique colour – not purple, but more like mauve, with an undertone of lilac – it would add a touch of international flare. Nobody had anything like it in Manyberries or for miles around. Six women immediately offered to go along as passengers.

I said I'd put a riding lawn mower in the parade and be the driver, if I had saved enough money by then to purchase one. I've been saving for a long time for a riding lawn mower because apart from a winning lottery ticket, it's about the only thing I've ever really, really wanted to own. My lawn is about 20 feet by 20 feet and most years there's grass if we get rain a few times in spring and summer. If I ever get one, I'll even offer to mow all the lawns in Manyberries.

By the time we'd compiled the list of all the parade participants, however, we were confronted with a worrisome problem. It seemed everybody in town and from all the ranches and farms around was going to be in the parade.

"We can't have a parade if there's nobody to watch it," said Perley.

"Maybe we could ask the people in Taber or up in Medicine Hat to come and watch the parade," Purvis said. Purvis wanted people from away to see how big his dog is. We thought it likely folks in those other towns and cities would have their own Dominion Day parades so that wasn't workable.

It was Harry Charles who came up with the solution. "It's pretty simple," he said. "Say the first float is Four-Eyed Tom with the dogs. What Tom does is bring his wife and she stands and watches the parade go by. When he rounds the corner and is out of sight, she runs back of the Ranchmen's and switches places with him. Tom then sprints back to where she was standing and watches the parade go by."

You have to admire Harry Charles' creative genius. Everybody just leaned back and stared at him, speechless in admiration.

"If I'm driving my Renault in the parade, I'll just switch places with one of my lady passengers and she can drive around and I can see the parade. Then she can switch places with another of the ladies when it's her turn to watch it go by."

It was going to take a long time from start to finish because some families have several members who can drive. Hazel offered up the Staples family as an example. "Mr. and Mrs. Staples, 19-year old Annie, 18-year old Lynda, 16-year old Jim Jr., and two more at 14 and 12. That means eight stops for them – their float will have to make the circle eight times if they're all going to be in the parade and all going to watch it."

Four-Eyed Tom spoke up to remind us he doesn't have a wife, never had a wife and didn't anticipate ever having one. He added that no woman in the world had been willing to get into the cab of his flatbed since his old dog had an accident on the passenger side of the seat. We weren't going to let that little problem slow down our Dominion Day freight train, however.

Ever since that night Perley and Harry Charles have been bent over the parade notebook at the Ranchmen's trying to calculate how many hours the parade is going to last.

You have to understand that Manyberries is not a metropolis, although the people who live here dream and think big. So it isn't the length of the parade route that has them calculating. It is how much time does it take for a family of eight to be in the parade and watch it at the same time? And multiply that family by dozens of others, some smaller, some larger and you could have a parade that starts before daylight and ends long after dark. There's a chance the parade might have to start July 1st and finish July 2nd.

One other complication is the age-old tradition in Manyberries that whenever a parade is held and finished, those bringing up the rear have to turn around and lead the parade back to the starting point.

I would not bet on our having a Manyberries Dominion Day parade next July 1st because of all the logistics and planning that has to be done.

But that's not a bad thing because it'll give me more time to save the money for my riding lawn mower.

The Naked Protest

Old Rutherford came in all excited, waving a months-old copy of a tabloid newspaper he had found on the bench beside the front door of the Ranchmen's.

"Did you see this about the big naked protest in Ottawa?"

"Large naked people were protesting in Ottawa?" Harry Charles asked. "Man, that makes my eyes hurt just thinking about it. On the other hand it'll be hard to argue that nothing interesting ever happens in Ottawa."

"It was probably the New Democrats protesting the sales tax on baby clothes, if there is such a tax," Perley was scowling. "Those people will protest at the drop of a hat. Guess they've graduated to protesting by dropping their drawers."

"Could have been the Liberals," Purvis offered, "protesting the election. Must have been tough on them, getting yanked right out of their silk underwear like that."

"No, no, it was a group of activists riding bicycles and trying to persuade Canadians that they can do their bit by getting out of their pickups and riding bicycles or walking to work." Old Rutherford laid the newspaper on the table where it began to dampen from spilled beer. "They were environmentalists."

"Not a lot of pickups in Ottawa," I said. "When I was there, the little pissant cars outnumbered real vehicles at least 10 to one. Most of them drove things like Harry Charles' little French station wagon."

"Geez, my eyes are hurting even more," Harry Charles said. "But I'll bet all those Japanese tourists on the buses made the Kodak film company happy. Can you imagine what it would look like, large naked people riding bicycles down and across and up and out of those potholes?"

Old Rutherford was exasperated, as he usually is when he tries to have a serious political conversation with the regulars in the Ranchmen's. "These were young people," he said very slowly, "most of them in their early to mid-20s, and they were persuading people to use alternative transportation, like bicycles. When I said big I didn't mean the people, I meant the protest. The media gave it a lot of attention."

"The media would be there in full force if they were naked and it wouldn't matter what they were protesting," I said. "If there'd been only one naked protestor she would have been the lead interview on Politics with Don Newman, and Mike Duffy Live, and Mansbridge and Robertson would have flown in from Toronto to have her do a re-ride for the National News."

"There were young men there as well," Rutherford said, leaning forward to re-scan the story, "and they should be respected, not mocked, for their idealism."

"Well, at least respected for the risks they took," Harry Charles said. "I don't think I'd ride naked on a bicycle where the best roads are in worse shape than our main street."

"I bet if we had an Annual Naked Bicycle Protest here in Manyberries we could draw some pretty big crowds," Purvis said, and you could see in his eyes he was already calculating where and how large the potential profits might be. "We could pick a different issue every year so nobody got left out."

"I'm proud of you, my boy," Perley said. "You're being inclusive, just like they keep telling us in Ottawa that we have to be."

"No, I'm just thinking that if you want to draw crowds you have to have a little something for everyone. If all you do is ride naked down the street to protest against one issue, all you're gonna draw is one-issue folks."

"Well, if it ever happened, I'd suggest the first protest be something to which young people would be drawn," I offered.

"I could agree with that," Old Rutherford said and he actually gave me an approving smile. I think he wonders sometimes if we take him seriously and he was pleased that he had at least started us thinking.

"You could be the Parade Marshal because you brought the idea to the table," Harry Charles said to Old Rutherford, who smiled and shook his head.

"With all due respect, which I have in abundance for Mr. Rutherford," Purvis said, "I think we'd want to have someone of national prominence leading the parade, someone who'd be guaranteed to draw the interest of the national media." I think we were all hoping Purvis wasn't going to volunteer.

And God Created Manyberries

"Yes, because that would lend credibility to the event and while I am well known to everybody here and some in Moose Jaw, I could hardly be described as a person of national prominence. An event of this magnitude would demand a person of equal stature."

"The problem is, not a lot of people around here get very excited about the environment," Harry Charles said. "You'd draw a bigger crowd of bikers if you were protesting low grain or beef prices."

"Won't matter at all what you decide to protest against," I said. "If you get a gang of naked bicycle riders out you'll have CBC relocating its headquarters from Toronto to Manyberries. Hell, if you do it every year, CBC will make it permanent."

"But you would still agree that the inaugural event should be linked to an issue that concerns young people?" Old Rutherford asked me.

"I would, and I'll even go out on the street to watch it instead of just looking out the window, if you can recruit the perfect Parade Marshal to lead it."

"Who did you have in mind?"

"I was thinking we'd need somebody who is recognized nationally and who, when you hear the name, you'd automatically want to be part of the parade."

"Like David Suzuki?"

"I wouldn't stand up at the window to watch David Suzuki ride by in the nude leading a parade," Perley said. "Not that I don't respect him, but he's probably older than Mr. Rutherford. And besides, he hates Alberta, or at least our politicians. Did you hear on CHAT what he said about Ed Stelmach?"

"I concur," Old Rutherford said. "We need a young person's issue. It's more about their future than ours so we need somebody of today's generation."

There was a pause as they all sipped their beer, except Old Rutherford, who wouldn't sit and take a sip from one of the full glasses because it would mean he'd have to stay and buy a round for the whole table.

"Do you think we could get a Hollywood movie star?" Four-Eyed Tom wondered.

"No, we need a Canadian. They keep talking about Canadian content on radio and television and besides, we're Canadians," Perley said.

"If it's about drawing national attention and participants there's only one possibility," I said. "Not even a possibility, it's essential." I paused to make sure they were paying attention.

"We need the Honourable Rona Ambrose to be our first Parade

Marshal. And she has visited the area at least once since she became a Member of Parliament."

"Well, she certainly has a high profile; Stephen just put her in charge of Intergovernmental Affairs. The guy who talks the news on CHAT said that on the radio this morning." That surprised me because I thought Old Rutherford, who prides himself on his British roots, would have been a CBC listener.

"So much the better, she can launch herself as Minister in charge of Intergovernmental Affairs."

"It seems to me that I still have a bicycle in the shed," Harry Charles said.

"I bet I could borrow my grandson's bike," was the response from Purvis.

"I couldn't ride a bicycle if I had to," Perley said, "but I don't mind walking in the parade if it's for the future and young people."

"I'll walk with you, Perley," Four-Eyed Tom said, "and I'll put up 10 dollars toward a bike for her to ride."

"I'll get a camera," I told them, "and record it for posterity."

It was at that point that Old Rutherford took his leave, satisfied that at last he had found something to arouse our political consciousness and instil in us a sense of civic duty and democratic responsibility.

The Manyberries Glow

One thing we have plenty of in Manyberries is sunshine and while we might not lead the world, or even Canada, in hours of sunshine per day, we are unchallenged in best overall individual suntan category. In fact, we boast ownership of the gold and silver medals in that event.

Our medallists are Old Rutherford and the Mrs. They are devotees of what Old Rutherford calls "gathering sunshine"; they never miss a day and are so dedicated they do their gathering stark naked. Not for them the skimpy outfits you see in pictures from Brazilian or French Riviera beaches. Nope, they do their gathering *au naturel* and it's probably a good thing. I'm not certain the human eye or mind could handle the sight of Old Rutherford in a thong or the Mrs in a string bikini.

Old Rutherford has made gathering sunshine a lifelong study. They go to places he claims deliver the most intense sunshine for whatever time of year it is. In winter, when the sun is lower on the horizon, they take what they can get through their south-facing living room window. It is said that if you look through their west-facing kitchen window late in the day you can see the Mrs preparing supper and catching the weakening rays of the sun as it settles in the west.

Those who have looked say she wears only an apron as she peels turnips that Old Rutherford grows all summer and puts up in his root cellar.

I have heard some of the women speak enviously of the beautiful tan that Old Rutherford's Mrs sports year round. On the other hand I've also heard them remark that her skin would probably make a fine matching purse and shoe ensemble.

You have to realize that it has been a long time since Old Rutherford and the Mrs described themselves as middle-aged. A very long time.

Anyway, I had just returned from 10 days in British Columbia where I was learning about working a gold claim from a friend who offered to teach me that business. In exchange for the knowledge he imparted I spent my time shovelling mud, hauling water, shovelling mud, prying boulders out of streambeds, shovelling mud, watching for grizzly bears, shovelling mud, cooking over an open fire, shovelling mud, setting up and taking down tents and, when there was time, shovelling mud. Bent stiff and weary, I rolled into the Ranchmen's to get caught up on the latest news.

The first thing I said when my eyes adjusted to the dark was a compliment to Hazel at the bar for how healthy she looked. "Were you away to some place warm and sunny?" I asked.

"Nope, you know I haven't taken a holiday since the first day I walked through that door," she said.

"Well, you've sure got a healthy glow," I said. "Maybe that alkaline water has long term health benefits. I'd like a beer with black rum on the side, please."

Over in the dark corner, Four-Eyed Tom was in his usual chair and I waved a hello at him. Tom leaned forward a little into the light and returned my wave.

I did a second take and looked closer. Four-Eyed Tom had a glow just like Hazel, in fact he had a better glow, and that was unusual. You see, Four-Eyed spends very little time in the outdoors in the sunshine. He went to pension early and spends most of his waking hours in the Ranchmen's working on crossword puzzles and reading old issues of Reader's Digest. It might have been the light but Four-Eyed looked almost carroty in colour.

It wasn't quite the high cocktail hour so I took up position at our table and caught up on the news from a week-old Calgary newspaper somebody had left on a chair. The high cocktail hour begins when Harry Charles, Perley and Purvis drop in for a round or two before supper.

Perley was the first to arrive, having finished his mail delivery. Actually his gunnysack was still bulging so he hadn't, in the strictest sense, finished his deliveries because his thirst trumped his sense of duty.

Harry Charles arrived a few minutes later and then Purvis arrived and took up his chair, which backs against the wall and gives him a good view of the whole room and the front entrance. In the old wild west days that might have marked him as an outlaw or even a lawman but Manyberries was never very wild. It's just that Purvis

And God Created Manyberries

has investments in a lot of areas and he likes to see who's coming and going and be up to date on everything that's happening. Harry Charles says Purvis watches roughnecks from the oil and gas wells for indications that the well they're drilling is showing any promise. I've seen Purvis walk casually by a roughneck in for a libation at the Ranchmen's and take a deep sniff for the scent of fresh crude oil or natural gas. If his nostrils flare you can bet good money that Purvis will hightail it out of the Ranchmen's and go home and make a telephone call to his stock broker up in Calgary. He claims you can actually smell it when a company hits oil or a gas pocket.

As Purvis was settling himself, Thor walked in looking for her husband. Her real name isn't Thor and I won't tell you what it is because I have to live here but she was given the name Thor by Harry Charles. He said it was because she reminded him of the lady who sings at the end of operas to let the audience know the thing is ending. I have never seen her wear a helmet with horns but I can imagine her keeping it handy by the door when her husband comes home late from the Ranchmen's without prior approval. It wouldn't surprise any of us if there's a trident right beside the helmet. Perley says he can remember when Thor was just a wafer of a girl, a mere slip of a thing back before she committed holy matrimony with her husband. She still wears her hair in pigtails and that, I guess, is why she appears so operatic. Not that very many people in operas likely wear knee-high construction boots.

Well, I glanced at Thor and then glanced again and then looked real hard. Thor was decidedly orange-coloured. She had about the same hue as Four-Eyed Tom, but more orangey than carroty.

Thor just glanced around the Ranchmen's and not seeing her husband turned and made an exit.

"Did you see the glow on Thor?" I asked the table. "She's got the same glow as Hazel at the bar and Four-Eyed Tom over in the corner. As I said to Hazel, all that alkaline water must be good for you after all."

"It is foolishness, that's what it is," Purvis said. "It's a great waste of good money and they're all doing it."

"Doing what? I asked. "Drinking too much water?"

"No, visiting Old Rutherford and the Mrs two or three days a week and foolishly spending their money," he replied.

I started to ask him what he meant but he waved me off, saying he didn't want to discuss such foolishness because it would spoil his drink now and his dinner later.

It was left to Perley to inform me that Old Rutherford and the Mrs had opened a sun tanning parlour and that most of the women in town were going there and paying good money to turn their hides orange.

"How and where would they possibly open a sun tanning parlour?" I wondered.

"Well," Harry Charles chimed in, "Old Rutherford heard that a sun tanning parlour had gone broke over in Taber and he went and bought all the equipment for 10 cents on the dollar. He had in mind that he and the Mrs would be able to set it up for themselves to use whenever it's cloudy."

"And Purvis is steamed because he didn't see the profit potential in it and Old Rutherford is raking in the cash," Perley added.

"It wasn't the profit potential I missed," Purvis told him in a bitter tone. "I didn't remember that old line that there's a sucker born every minute and that Manyberries has its unfair share of foolish women with too much time and money on their hands. "And," he paused, "not to forget Four-Eyed Tom, who's wasting his pension just as foolishly as all those women are wasting money they should be spending on groceries."

"Well, you could look at it as a new industry for Manyberries and one that contributes to the overall health of the female population," I said. "I read somewhere that we all need exposure to the sun to get our daily recommended dose of Vitamin D."

"I wouldn't bet good money that those tanning machines provide Vitamin D," Harry Charles said. "But those women aren't going to Margaritaville for vitamins, anyway – they're going to get tanned."

"Margaritaville? Like the song on the jukebox by that Jimmy Buffet?"

"Yep, that's what Old Rutherford and the Mrs are calling that little trailer they have in the backyard where they installed the tanning machines."

"And get this," said Perley, "they're serving peenus colatchamacallits, without alcohol of course because they don't want to compete with the Ranchmen's."

"Well, you know a tan makes a person look healthy," I offered, "and I've always liked the look of a well-tanned girl. I especially like tan lines but that's because in the old days the girls in Playboy magazine all had tan lines. I guess it's true that we are influenced by what we read at an early age."

"It's also true that if you had read a bit more and looked at pictures less, you might have developed some influence among your peers," Harry Charles said, rather snidely I thought.

"Well, they're not all wearing bathing suits, or bikinis, according to what we're hearing," Perley told me. "Some of those who might still be able to wear bikinis are doing their tanning in the altogether. And some of those who shouldn't even wear a bathing suit are doing the same. Still, there must be a few sporting tan lines, if you're of a mind to do some checking."

"Not me," I said quickly. "And don't you even suggest anywhere beyond this table that I might be interested in checking for tan lines because I like living and I like living here."

"Just joshing," said Perley.

It was just then that Mrs. Purvis arrived. I stood and offered my chair and grabbed an unoccupied one from the next table.

"My, you certainly have a healthy glow," I told her. Truth is she had a glow but it was an orange one and she appeared to have been using carrot juice as a moisturizer.

Mrs. Purvis extended her arm and moved her watchband up her arm a little to reveal a thin white strip of skin. Mrs. Purvis is not a small lady but she's not as a big as Thor.

"I keep the watch on to see how much progress I'm making in my tanning," she told me.

"Well, it's obvious to me that you're making real progress," I said. "Why, that white strip on your wrist is as pale as the skin on a new born baby."

"It's the only tan line I have," and she giggled.

Purvis glared at me, daring me to even think something. I didn't accept the challenge.

"How much does Old Rutherford charge for a session?" I asked, changing the subject.

"They're paying $2.50 for a half hour in that foolish machine," Purvis blurted. "And they're lined up waiting to get in there and waste their money."

Mrs. Purvis wasn't staying for a drink. She had just dropped in to tell Purvis not to be late for dinner because she was preparing Hawaiian beach ham steaks with canned pineapple slices. "And rum and coconut milk cocktails which they call piña coladas."

When she left, Purvis leaned over and into the middle of the table. "If you guys want in on it, I have a potentially very profitable little idea in which to invest," he said.

"If it involves shovelling mud while looking for gold, count me out," I said.

"No, no, this is a good one, a sure bet. I've got a line on a lotion that puts a dye on a woman and one bottle will keep her tanned pretty near the whole year round. I'm going to order a few cases and cut Hazel in if she sells it at the bar. You guys can get in on it too, if you want."

"How much does it cost?" asked Perley.

"I can get it by the case at two dollars a bottle. We sell it at $10 a bottle and give Hazel 50 cents a unit and we split the remaining $7.50 four ways."

"That might drive Old Rutherford and the Mrs out of business," Harry Charles said.

"I don't think I'd want to invest in something that would compete with the first new industry that's come to town in years," Perley said.

"It's free enterprise," Purvis insisted. "That's what makes this a great nation. People toiling and grubbing and sweating and investing and making a profit. And, if we do it right, we won't even have to claim it as income."

"But Purvis," I said, "if this is a lotion and a woman rubs it all over to get her tan, how does she get a tan line?"

"There's the million dollar question," Harry Charles said. "If a woman gets a tan from your lotion and shows no evidence of tan lines, people could wind up speculating that she's genetically orange, or that she prances around naked in some place that turns her that colour."

"Maybe I can get a small paint brush and very carefully paint the lotion on," Purvis was thinking out loud. "Did you save any of those old Playboy magazines so I can figure out where to stop and start?"

And God Created Manyberries

Terrorizing Manyberries

Perley came into the Ranchman's wearing his official postal cap and when we saw him we knew he was on official federal business because he rarely wears the cap even when he's sorting mail or delivering it.

It's not actually an official postal cap – it's a skipper's cap that Harry Charles wore when he owned a 32 foot steel hulled cruiser on the Great Lakes. When Harry Charles sold his boat and moved out here he had no further use for the cap so he gave it to Perley. It still has a few fish hooks dangling from it and Perley wears it with pride whenever he has to do anything federally official like leading the July 1st parade, if we ever have one.

Perley had a pretty stern look as he pulled his chair back and joined us for the cocktail hour.

"The guy who talks the news on CHAT says terrorism is a threat to all of North America and that Canada is not immune to this pandemetric," he told us, while waving a hand with two fingers extended to Hazel at the bar. That signals to her that he wants a beer with a gin chaser. Perley believes that gin is the drink of choice among senior federal bureaucrats.

"The thing of it is the news guy said the terrorists are targeting the oil and gas industry because they don't like our religion. And the new Premier, Ed Stelmach, says we have to be vigilant."

"Well, that's another worry I can forget about," Harry Charles heaved a sigh of relief. "First, there's no infrastructure in Manyberries and second, we don't have a church, at least not one that anyone has attended in the last who knows how many years. So not much chance the pandemic will hit here."

"That's complacency," Perley said, "and complacency is the enemy of peace, safety in the streets, order in society and good government."

"I'd argue that politicians are the enemy of all that," Harry Charles countered, "but it seems to me that was the topic for debate last night and the night before and nobody disagreed. What's on your mind, Perley?"

"What's the distance from here to the border? Well, I don't know exactly either but any of us could walk it in a day and a terrorist who's physically fit could do it in less."

"But why would a terrorist want to come from the U.S. to Manyberries?" Purvis was as sceptical as the rest of us. "Hell, we can't even get tourists to come here except for the odd one who gets lost in the summer."

"That's my point," said Perley. "Nobody would ever think of Manyberries as a hideout for terrorists who'd come here and use it as a jumping-off place. Why, they could sneak across the border, hole up here and then go down and bomb Toronto."

There was a long pause as we all closed our eyes to picture Toronto disappearing.

Finally, Harry Charles asked Perley what his solution was, assuming he'd had enough time to arrive at one between his last mail drop and his arrival at our table.

"We need a vigilante committee here in Manyberries. We should get some of the boys together who can stay up past nine and set up regular patrols to watch for suspicious goings-on, especially in the summer when it's warm enough to walk up here from the border."

"Geez, you wouldn't be thinking they should arm themselves, are you Perley?" Harry Charles seemed a little nervous about where Perley was going. "Having some of these guys wandering around town with their deer rifles late at night is more likely to create nightmares than a sense of security."

"Yes, but we'd only pick the best and brightest, the most stalwart and steady. And nobody is going to mistake Hazel for a terrorist when she closes down here and we all go home."

"It's going to take a long time to recruit your team if you're going to pick only the best and brightest," Purvis told Perley. "And if stalwart means sturdy, you're going to have a lot of women on your committee."

"I think if I were you, Perley, I'd phone the Mounties and get their opinion before you start organizing and recruiting. Seems to me I read somewhere they don't respond kindly to people taking the law into their own hands." Harry Charles was obviously not greatly excited about organizing a terrorist vigilante committee.

"Not that I don't take the terrorist threat seriously," he continued, "but I think something as critically important as this should be coordinated with the federal authorities."

"What would you call it and who would lead the Manyberries Terrorist Vigilante Committee?" Purvis was leaning toward siding with Perley.

"Well, I am the face of federalism in Manyberries through my postal obligations, so I'd be willing to co-chair such a committee with somebody like yourself." Perley has pretty sharp political and fishing instincts and knows how to set a hook.

"I can see that this idea of yours is taking shape and developing momentum," Harry Charles said, "and maybe it's a good thing knowing our three streets will be patrolled at night and we can sleep without fear of a terrorist invasion. But I'd suggest you might give some thought to what you call this committee."

"What's wrong with Manyberries Terrorist Vigilante Committee?" Purvis asked. "It covers the bases, makes it clear what it's all about. And vigilante is a well known practice and word here in the west."

"Well, yes, in the American west," Harry Charles responded. "But in the Canadian west we didn't do that sort of thing, and people might make the mistake of thinking you guys and your recruits are a bunch of crazy coots who are wannabe gunslingers from the movies."

"Well, that's how much they might know," Perley said rather huffily.

"Yes, and the last thing you want to happen is having those effete eastern news people mocking you. It wouldn't do much for the image of Manyberries if all those Toronto newspapers started poking fun at us."

"Well, if we don't call ourselves vigilantes, what can we call us?" Perley usually defers to the wisdom of Harry Charles, who always reads all the news so extensively.

"What the free world needs in the fight against terrorism is vigilance, and that means it is incumbent on all to be vigilant, cautious and aware of anything unusual, including the presence of strange behaviour by strangers," Harry Charles said as both Perley and Purvis hung on every word.

"So I'd call your committee the Manyberries Awareness Committee and restrict membership to two of the most stolid and influential individuals in the community. And they should act as co-chairs of the committee to avoid confusion, overlap and unreliable people. And I stress stolid in terms of the individuals you choose."

"What about night patrols and guards when the town is sleeping?" Perley shifted his postman's cap so it angled more to one side and down a little over his forehead in a somewhat cocky Humphrey Bogart fashion.

"That would be the responsibility of the two key men running the operation. You just can't leave duties like that to men who don't have the steel in their spines or the steady nerves of born leaders."

"I'd nominate Perley for that," said Purvis.

"And I'd nominate Purvis," Perley returned the favour.

"So we can start tonight, looking for people who shouldn't be prowling the streets when everybody else is in bed." Purvis was anxious to get started. Like most people Purvis is always looking for something that adds a little spice to life.

"You start whenever you want, but... there is... one... caveat," Harry Charles said in a hushed voice. "You can't talk about this because that's the one rule in the intelligence and spying communities, they don't talk about what they do. If this got out to the newspapers in Medicine Hat or Lethbridge, it'd only be a day or two before it hit the Toronto newspapers and that is when the bad stuff hits the fan. Oh, one other thing, you can't look for swarthy dark-skinned people if you have that in mind because that would be racial stereotyping and that has been outlawed by Ottawa."

"Yeah, that's a point," said Perley. "But can we tell you guys about our operation and what we're doing?"

"You can rest assured I will never betray your confidence," Harry Charles said. "And I trust that you," he turned to me, "will offer a similar assurance?"

I gave him the most fervent assurance I could, thinking that if some of my Ottawa acquaintances ever got wind of the fact that I was even in the same room as this conversation I'd be banned from there forever. Later, on second thought, I realized that being banned from Ottawa forever wouldn't be such a catastrophe in anybody's book.

When they left, Perley and Purvis sauntered with their thumbs hooked into their belts, sort of like Pierre Trudeau during his Prime Ministerial gunslinger days.

"I'll sleep sounder knowing there's nobody out there with deer rifles patrolling our three streets," Harry Charles told me. "It occurred to me they'd be looking for swarthy, dark-skinned people and I was worried about Old Rutherford and the Mrs because they're so well tanned."

"Seems to me," I said to Harry Charles, "there could be a disaster with guys walking around itching to hang a terrorist's skin on their trophy walls and some woman wearing a kerchief out for a late night stroll to the outhouse."

"Well, no need to worry," he said. "Fact is, those two don't stay awake beyond 8:30, and when they do get up at night it's to heed the call of nature. It'd be a shame if somebody who knew what he

And God Created Manyberries

was doing took this on and actually found a terrorist." He paused and grinned.

"I don't know how I'd while away the evening hours without spending at least a few minutes imagining Toronto being transformed back into what used to be some of the best agricultural land in the world."

Spicering up Manyberries

During the last antelope hunting season we were sitting in the Ranchmen's like, as Harry Charles put it, "crows on a fence," watching the hunters arrive for their three-day hunts. Harry Charles uses that expression whenever he walks into a new saloon or coffee shop because it accurately describes what the permanent citizens do when strangers enter. All heads swivel and watch the newcomers enter and then slowly turn as they make their way to a table. Harry Charles says crows do that: sit silently and turn their heads to watch the approach and slowly follow whatever it is they're watching until it's either out of sight or finds a table at which to sit.

Anyway, we were sitting there and a very fancy couple walked in and found a table over near the shuffleboard and signalled Hazel at the bar for a drink. They were dressed like something you might see in a Toronto magazine. Both were wearing very tailored trousers and blaze orange jackets and, under the jackets, what looked like silky black and red plaid shirts. The boots they were wearing were fashionable, soft suede and just over ankle-high. They looked too thin to ward off a grasshopper bite and around Manyberries we have a lot of those. We also have a lot of rattlesnakes and that's why I am still looking for cast iron footwear that reaches above my knees. In the meantime, I wear knee-high boots when I'm out on the prairie in rattlesnake season.

Anyway, this couple were almost too beautiful for Manyberries and we were reminded of the time Keith Spicer came to visit us. Keith Spicer was an easterner who travelled across Canada as Chairman of something called the Citizens' Forum on Canada's Future. That was back in 1990-91 and for reasons known to nobody but perhaps Keith Spicer the CFCF came to Manyberries. We heard later that Mr.

And God Created Manyberries

Spicer calculated he had heard from 700,000 Canadians on Canada's shape, values and priorities.

A lot of us in Manyberries figured that Canada was in pretty good shape but that maybe the main street could use a little scraping if we could raise the cash to hire a road grader. We also felt that Canada was pretty valuable but Mr. Spicer said that wasn't the sort of values he had in mind. Some of the people who came with him told us that our priorities were much the same as the priorities of other Canadians from sea to sea to sea. That made us feel pretty good, knowing we had so much in common with other Canadians. We were delighted to learn that bilingualism and biculturalism were unifying priorities. We just hadn't known they were Manyberries priorities. I think it was about that time that Harry Charles decided he just had to buy a Renault station wagon and that was a move he never regretted. The ladies in Manyberries just adored that little French wagon, and Harry Charles couldn't drive downtown without some woman waving him down to hitch a ride.

We'd read in one of the city newspapers somebody left at the Ranchmen's that Keith Spicer had said if you want to learn French, you should sleep with a French woman. Well, Harry Charles' beloved Irene was born in Utah and raised for a time in England and eastern Canada and didn't speak French so it could be the Renault was the most acceptable alternative.

Anyway, when Mr. Spicer came to town he decided to dress as he was informed that everyone else did in Manyberries and we thought that was very thoughtful of him.

I once saw a picture of Oscar Wilde when he toured the wild American west. Oscar wore a hat with a brim wide enough to give shade to the wearer and a horse, if he was riding one. The brim on Mr. Spicer's hat was even wider. Now, it can get sunny out on the prairie and you don't have to strain your eyes trying to spot a cowboy hat in any crowd. But even cowboys have limits as to brim widths and we guessed Mr. Spicer, being from Ottawa and all, didn't know it doesn't get that sunny around Manyberries. Harry Charles said that brim was so wide you could see Mr. Spicer coming before he turned the corner of one of the few blocks in town.

At the end of it all, it was a great Citizens' Forum on Canada's Future and everybody agreed we should do it again sometime. We have something similar every night at the Ranchmen's but we've never had a Chairman with a hat brim so wide he could knock down bystanders if he turned his head.

We were very pleased to be active participants in that great Canadian experience. We were also pleased to learn that we were an important multilingual and multicultural part of the great Canadian mosaic. We were so pleased to hear that we were multicultural and multilingual that we made arrangements to get some imported German dill pickles at the Ranchmen's. Of course we weren't going to stop eating the dill pickles we buy from the Hutterites down the road but we thought a little multicultural variety never hurt anyone. Hazel already stocks red and white wine so there was no room for improvement there but she said she'd check out the prices on American and other foreign beers to see if she could culturally enhance the cooler. She rewrote the label on the two gallon jar on the bar and now people can order pickled oeufs and, from the menu, scrambled oeufs. She didn't raise the price on either item, which we thought was very reasonable of her.

When I later mentioned that Mr. Spicer's hat resembled the one worn by Oscar Wilde in that old photograph in a magazine, Harry Charles looked startled.

"Apart from the hat, I don't think there are many similarities between Oscar Wilde and Keith Spicer," he said. Harry Charles reads a lot and knows more about a lot of stuff than most anybody in Manyberries. "Oscar Wilde was a very flamboyant man," he said. "In fact, he was so flamboyant he got sent to jail and that's where or perhaps why he wrote the Ballad of Reading Gaol."

"I remember that poem from junior high school," I said. "I think one of the lines was 'Each man kills the thing he loves' but I thought it was probably about hunting and respecting the birds and animals we bring home to eat."

"Better go back and read it again," Harry Charles said, "if you can find your old schoolbooks. And if you do find them you'll discover how little you knew back then and how much you've forgotten since. Anyway, when I say Oscar Wilde was flamboyant, I mean *really* flamboyant."

"That's pretty inflammatory," Perley chimed in.

"I don't know what you guys are talking about," Purvis said. What's wrong with being flamboyant, and if Keith Spicer wants to be as flamboyant as Oscar Wilde, why shouldn't he be? I mean, hell, it was a wide brim but geez, he's probably never been out of Ottawa and maybe somebody told him the sun was a lot stronger than it really is."

"It ain't the hat that makes the man," Harry Charles said, further confusing Purvis. Then he winked at Perley and they both chuckled. "But from what I observed while he was here and from what I've read, Keith Spicer could never be described as in the same flamboyant category as Oscar Wilde."

"Could be Mr. Spicer saw that old photo of Oscar Wilde and thought one like it only with a wider brim would look good on him," Purvis speculated.

Harry Charles leaned over and whispered something to Purvis while Perley and I watched and waited for his reaction.

"Oh," Purvis said. His eyebrows were up near his hairline. "Oh, well, who was to know? The Marquis of Queensbury? Really? The guy who made up the rules for boxing?"

Harry Charles and Perley looked at him solemnly and nodded.

I never got around to it because I kept forgetting but it was my intent to write a letter to Mr. Spicer to tell him if he came back to Manyberries, it'd probably be wise not to wear a hat like the one Oscar Wilde wore when he visited America. I even thought of sending him a John Deere tractor cap if I hadn't had need of it myself.

One thing I have noticed, Purvis never wears his broadest brimmed hat around town anymore.

The Great Equalizer

Purvis was reading a week-old copy of the Calgary Herald when Perley, Harry Charles and I walked into the Ranchmen's.

We get our newspapers from either the men's room at the Ranchmen's or off the bench at the front door on those days when it's warm enough to sit outside and read them. There's always some management type from one of the big oil or natural gas companies passing through town who generously leaves them after they're read. It's an inexpensive way to keep up on what's happening in the world. For really important information, like the weather, we listen to CHAT radio up in Medicine Hat.

"Did you see this?" Purvis was waving the front section of the paper. It was a Thursday edition so there was a stack of flyers advertising for sophisticated big-city emporiums like Wal-Mart, which interested us more than the actual news stuff. If you held a vote at our table it'd be unanimous that what our town really needs is a Wal-Mart where you can buy just about anything made anywhere in the world. Of course we'd still do some shopping in Taber and Medicine Hat because they have other establishments that have VLT machines. But it'd be very handy to have Wal-Mart here if you were ever in urgent need of a hammer or new underwear.

"In Ottawa, they're talking about spreading the money around so everybody gets a fair share, no matter what province they call home."

"That so?" said Perley. "Hope they can find it in their hearts to remember pensioners. Last raise I got in my pension was just enough to buy one extra loaf of bread every six months."

"Yep, according to the Herald here, they're calling it critically important to the future of the country. Some of the Premiers are

And God Created Manyberries

saying if they don't get more money from Ottawa, they can't guarantee that their provinces will want to remain in Canada. The rest are saying if they have to give more to the others, they can't guarantee their provinces will want to remain in Canada."

"It's the age old argument," Harry Charles said. "Everybody gives too much and nobody ever gets enough."

"Exactly, and it's time we let somebody know that Manyberries has been giving way more than our fair share and getting back way less." If there's anybody in Manyberries who is obsessed with getting his fair share, it's Purvis.

Harry Charles waved at Hazel at the bar, holding up a handful of fingers plus one to let her know we needed six glasses. "It has always vexed me," he said, "that places like Medicine Hat or even Taber get more money than we get here in Manyberries. The government up there says it distributes our money on a per capita basis but I think that's a smoke screen to hide the real reason. They do it because they can get more votes out of those places than from here." I didn't believe for one minute that Harry Charles was serious and decided he was just giving Purvis a little jump start to get the conversation rolling.

"That's crass and cynical politics," Purvis said. "Why should they get more money just because there are more voters there than here?"

"I really don't care if Taber gets more money than Manyberries," Perley interjected, "I'd just like to see them give my pension a big boost. These Premiers are out for one thing, and that's their own self-interest. It's about time they took a look at my pension and recognized that it's downright unfair. Hell, if I didn't have that triplex in Taber fully rented, I might have a hard time living on what I get from the government."

"That would be my point as well," Purvis responded. "If I didn't have my investments, the land I rent out, and the profits from the cow-calf operation with my sons, I'd have a devil of a time getting by on the few hundred dollars I get from Ottawa."

"So the two of you are arguing for equalization?" Harry Charles asked. "You both figure that Ottawa should sharpen its pencil and calculate how much you're being short-changed?"

"Don't see why not. Of course I'd never ask for anything more than my fair share. I don't know about Purvis, but all I want is what's coming to me and not a penny more."

"I agree with Perley. I don't want to be like the typical Canadian holding both hands out for more money from the government. I just want my fair share." Purvis held up two fingers to signal Hazel that she should add two more to the tray Harry Charles had ordered.

"What if the federal government decides that the formula for equalization should take into account the money Alberta gets from oil and gas revenues?" Harry Charles was headed somewhere but you wouldn't know it by the blandly innocent look on his face.

"There's absolutely no way they should even think about that," Purvis answered. "Those are disappearing resources and besides, they belong to Alberta, not the rest of that gimme gimme gang of Premiers."

"What if the federal government decided the cash rent Perley collects from his tenants should be included in his income and the cash you get when you sell your calves to the butcher should be included in yours? Those bureaucrats might decide you should pay more in the interests of equalization."

Both Perley and Purvis sputtered a little.

"That's off the topic, Harry Charles," Purvis scolded. "We're not talking about socialism here or even communism. We're talking about how much – no, we're talking about how *little* we get from Ottawa."

"Purvis is right. What he gets from the butcher for his calves and what I get from my tenants is none of the government's business. Besides that, I pay the butcher less than I would at a store when I pay him cash and my tenants pay lower rent for cash than they would in other places. So everybody benefits."

After Purvis and Perley left, Harry Charles shook his head and sighed.

"You know, I would wager that the conversations the Premiers have when they get together to negotiate equalization is very much like the conversation we just had with those two."

"Right," I said. "By the way, can you tell me who the butcher is who charges less for meat from the Purvis calves if you pay cash?"

Harry Charles just looked at me, sighed, and shook his head.

And God Created Manyberries

Hardball Politics
Manyberries Style

We were reading a newspaper from Calgary that somebody left in the men's room at the Ranchmen's a while back and all the news was about a Judge Gomery reporting that some politicians were crooked and did crooked things.

Harry Charles and Perley both read the newspaper over twice to see if any of our politicians were in on the crookedness and were relieved to find their names weren't mentioned.

We don't see our politicians here too often but we don't feel underrepresented or even ignored because of that.

In Manyberries we've often voted for the least popular person in the district at the provincial and federal levels because it gets them out of town.

At the municipal level you've gotta vote for candidates you like because their job doesn't take them all that far away and they could drop in at the Ranchmen's any time of the day or night. The last thing you want is a visit from a politician you don't like.

Our present provincial and federal politicians are exceptions to the usual practice, being that they're both nice guys and pretty popular with just about everybody but the closet Liberals and New Democrats, who don't seem to like anybody. They're in the political closet because the last thing you want is to be identified as a Liberal or a New Democrat if you're sitting in the Ranchmen's late of an evening.

Hazel at the bar tried to ban all conversations about politics, religion, ex-wives and ex-husbands, CBC television and Toronto because they tended to be divisive. She had to relent, however, on some of those topics.

Conversations about ex-wives and ex-husbands are verboten by mutual community agreement because you could be complaining about your ex-wife to the guy she married or his ex-wife. Even ex-husband and ex-wife jokes are interdicted because there's a very risky chance somebody might take it personally and the last thing you want at the Ranchmen's is some man or woman taking something personally and going on the prod. "Going on the prod" in cowboy language means throwing things at people, like chairs or bottles, even ones that aren't empty.

The last time we had an exciting political event in Manyberries was when Purvis thought we should have an election for our Sort-Of Postmaster and Sort-Of Postal delivery man, a job that Perley has been doing for years.

It doesn't pay Perley anything but he gets to visit people and they reward him with a drink now and then if he has time to stop and chat (and Perley always has time for that).

But Purvis, who saw the job as a stepping stone to something politically bigger, thought he'd like to take over Perley's job and proposed there be an election.

Now both Perley and Purvis are pretty popular old guys in Manyberries and there's always a chair at any table for them at the Ranchmen's so we braced ourselves for a divisive election.

Most of the women sided with Purley, as did Harry Charles and a few of the rest of us. But Purvis had his supporters, among a lot of the men, because he often helped them turn their gardens over in spring with his little Ford tractor.

Hazel at the bar had to remain officially neutral because you can't afford to rile any customers at the Ranchmen's since there just aren't that many. But she secretly supported Perley.

Harry Charles agreed to be Perley's campaign chairman and I said I'd be his communications agent in case any media took an interest in the election.

Purvis, always cocky, said he'd manage his own campaign and communications and whatever else anybody did in election campaigns.

It was agreed that the vote would be by secret ballot, the polling station would be the church nobody attends, and the vote would be on a Saturday one hour before the Ranchmen's opened for business.

In the campaign Purvis charged that Perley was only a part-timer who disappeared every September and only came back to the job in December when the hunting season ended. Even Purvis' own supporters booed him for that because so does everybody else.

Perley countered by saying he was experienced, honest, visionary and dependable. He pointed out, correctly, that the floor of the mailbox building hadn't been littered once since he took over the job. And, he added, not once had a pamphlet or literature from the New Democratic Party found its way into anybody's home. Perley drew a lot of applause for that last comment, even from Purvis supporters.

Unbeknownst to our campaign, Harry Charles had borrowed a very old school bus that had long been sitting in a neighbour's backyard waiting to be converted into a motor home. He hand painted two banners for the sides of the bus and all he put on them was four words: Go Postal With Perley. He rolled it up outside the Ranchmen's a few minutes before opening time and when Purvis saw it, he knew he was up against a professional political campaign team.

Not to be outdone, Purvis borrowed a real motor home from a guy at the west end of town who bought it when they discovered natural gas on land he was leasing. It was a magnificent thing, almost Taj Mahal-like in its stateliness with the orange shag carpeting and everything.

Harry Charles announced that the Perley bus would be available to anyone who wanted a ride to the polling station and back to the Ranchmen's afterwards. He said there would be tubs with beer on ice and bags of nachos compliments of the Go Postal With Perley campaign.

Purvis made the same offer to his supporters but said in addition to beer, there'd be Scotch and Alberta Sipping Whiskey and cheese from the Hutterites and pickled eggs. In addition, he promised, the Purvis for Postal Service bus would take the long way around, which meant it would go north four miles and cut west four miles, back south and then east, for a total of 16 miles. That would give them plenty of time to consume the complimentary food and refreshments. That got Purvis so much applause he said the motor home would leave earlier and allow for a stop along the way so they could get out and stretch their legs. Even more applause for that one.

Well, voting day came and Harry Charles began driving all over town picking up Perley campaign team members, supporters and voters. Everybody saw the Purvis land yacht leave town and head north and were a bit despondent because it was so packed there were people looking out the window of the little toilet room in the thing. And Purvis had done a pretty good job on the banners because he paid the junior high school art class to paint them for him.

The only guys smiling on our bus were Harry Charles and Perley and those smiles reminded me of the smile I saw on the face of a guy who won the nomination to be the official candidate for the New Democratic Party in the last federal election. It's sort of like the guy who bluffs in a poker game with no hand at all and one of the other players who doesn't have one either but has had two or three drinks more calls the bluff.

The Ranchmen's opens at 11:00, so voting had been set for 10:00 to 10:45 to give people on the buses time to vote before the doors were unlocked.

Perley's people were out in full force and they all gave him the thumbs up when they went behind the gunnysack to cast their votes. The rest of us thought it was false bravado because we all knew how many were going show up any minute when the Purvis bus arrived.

By 10:30 people were going to the window to see if the Purvis caravan was on its way but it was nowhere to be seen. By 10:35 Purvis' wife, who had arrived early to vote, was outside looking up the road but still no bus in sight.

By 10:40 the Perley team was getting excited. Only five minutes to go and no matter what, the poll would close sharp at 10:45 even if voters were in the room and in line.

Mrs. Purvis was looking pretty glum and Three-Eyed Tom didn't look too happy either when the big hand slipped up to 44.

At 10:45, Hazel announced the polls were closing and said she was pretty certain we all knew the outcome but the votes would still be counted and scrutineered back at the Ranchmen's.

We all piled into the old school bus and headed the several hundred feet back to the Ranchmen's and even took Mrs. Purvis and Three-Eyed Tom along so they could watch the ballot counting. There was still no sign of the Purvis castle on wheels.

Hazel counted the ballots as she took them out of the galvanized milk bucket, and it was a landslide for Perley. There was only one ballot for Purvis and nobody wanted to embarrass Mrs. Purvis by turning and looking at her. In Manyberries, we believe once the campaign is over and the ballots counted, we should go back to being civil to each other.

Finally, Purvis and his supporters arrived and Purvis conceded defeat in a speech that we thought was too florid and way too humble for Purvis.

One of his supporters said they got headed west on the road four miles north and thought when the coach stopped, it was so they could stretch their legs. But the reason was they'd run out of gas because nobody had checked the fuel gauge when they left. The guy who owned it said he was certain he had filled it some months before, but that tank was bone dry.

And God Created Manyberries

Nobody on the Purvis side was heart-broken and in fact were all very happy. That's because while they waited for somebody with a jerry can of gas to drive by they had finished off the beer, Scotch, sipping whiskey, Hutterite cheese and pickled eggs. Most of them crowded around Perley to congratulate him, as people do when somebody wins big in an election and might become a person of influence in the community.

Late in the evening a few of us were still in the Ranchmen's reminiscing about the campaign and some of the great and some of the god-awful things that had happened.

I said I was pretty pessimistic when I saw the Purvis bus roll out of town with all those supporters and figured that without a miracle, it was all over for Perley.

Perley said all he could do was smile like somebody who'd just lost a poker hand by bluffing wildly.

I remarked that Harry Charles had that same smile, so everybody must have thought the election was lost before we even got to the polling station.

Harry Charles smiled and said he didn't have any such smile at all. He said he was not only optimistic, he would have made a large wager that Perley would win.

I challenged that and said the smile he and Perley had on their faces gave them away and Perley had admitted it.

"That was the kind of smile you see on a person suffering gas pains," he said. "And I had gas pains."

I started to argue but he held up a finger. "There are two kinds of gas pains," he said. "There's the gas pains you get from certain foods and there's the gas pains you get from gas."

He now had a big grin on his face and both Perley and I caught on at the same time to what he was telling us.

"So how many gallons did you get?" Perley asked.

"We don't measure in gallons anymore, Perley," Harry Charles said. "But if I had to guess, I'd say I got nearly 15 gallons into the old school bus. If they ever do convert that thing into a motor home they'll have enough to get to Montana and most of the way back."

Ms Stronach Goes
to Manyberries

I think it was the spring of 2006 that Purvis told us he had heard a report on CHAT radio that a new book on Belinda Stronach had a lot of juicy stuff about her affairs. "The guy who talks the news says the relevations, according to observers in Ottawa, couldn't have come at a worse time for her because of the Ti Domi affair."

"That'd be *revelations*, Purvis", Harry Charles said, "and I think her worst time is behind her. In fact I think her worst time was when she decided to get into politics, but that's just my own personal observation."

Harry Charles gets a lot of newspapers mailed to him and reads them all and is probably Manyberries' most astute political observer. In his younger days, and they go back a very long way, he was courted by the Progressive, the Conservative, the Progressive Conservative, Liberal and Social Credit parties to run as a candidate federally and provincially. He refused, saying that if he had wanted to spend his time going door to door he would have applied for a job as a mailman.

"Maybe, but this is worse," Purvis argued. "I mean, after all, Ti Domi's wife said Belinda has been stepping out with her husband which, if true, would make Belinda an adulterator. Even a Liberal wouldn't vote for a woman who's been accused of adulterating."

"I don't know about that, Purvis," Harry Charles said. "Fact is, I think when politicians get tired of adulterating, to use your word, the taxpayers, they busy themselves adulterating each other. They just see that as a natural right of the horizontally mobile."

"I don't know what the hell you're talking about but I do know if people around here believe that if she stepped out with a married man with young children, they're not gonna vote for Belinda."

"Purvis, around here, people aren't going to vote for Belinda no matter what she did or who she did it to. This is Alberta, not Toronto. Anyway, I never was a Leafs follower."

"What does hockey have to with this scandal, for heaven's sake?"

"A better question is why in heaven's name something this tawdry deserves the sort of news coverage you'd see if somebody declared World War Three?"

"Well, she's beautiful and glamorous and famous, sort of like that girl singer Madonna."

"You're the beholder, Purvis, so whatever is in your eye is yours to own."

"Maybe we could get her to come here to do a fundraiser for the Manyberries Riding Academy. I read that she knows how to sit a horse."

Purvis was referring to the plan to make the Manyberries School into the new Manyberries Riding Academy. Because horses are an important part of our history and culture, the plan is to provide daily horsemanship lessons. In the interests of equality, I suggested to Perley, Purvis and Harry Charles that they should also offer horsewomanship lessons but they sneered at me.

But the riding academy school was considered such a grand idea they dragged Ian Tyson down from the foothills back in the fall of '04 to do a fundraiser for a riding arena and had a sell-out concert. Of course, they could sell out the community hall every night to just the women in the district if Ian decided he wanted a year round job.

"She probably learned to ride one of those postage stamp saddles that the Brits use," Perley commented.

"I don't know how anybody, Brit or otherwise, can sit a saddle without a horn and cantle. They probably don't even have real saddles where she comes from."

"Well, hell, we wouldn't ask her to ride a horse. All she'd have to do is make a speech and tell people to donate generously. I bet we'd get people coming down all the way from Medicine Hat just to see her. Geez, we could build an even bigger arena if we got some of those rich guys from up there giving us money. Maybe they'd even come down from Calgary."

"You'd probably have them coming from Toronto," Harry Charles offered. "Money draws people like a stockyard draws flies. You have to ask if you want people from Toronto walking the streets of Manyberries, even if there are only three or four streets in the whole town."

"I don't think folks would mind and I don't think it would harm Manyberries in any way if Belinda Stronach walked our streets," Purvis said.

"I'm not talking about Belinda," Harry Charles said, "I'm talking about those Toronto Bay Street types. The main street would be choked with BMW convertibles and what-not. One of them would scuff his loafer and either start suing us or pushing for us to get the roads paved."

"Yeah, but look at it this way, it'd give Three-Eyed Tom something to pee on other than pickups. And I don't mean on Belinda," Perley assured us, "I mean all those Toronto BMWs."

"Maybe I'll write her a letter," Purvis mused. "I'll ask her if she's ever in the area if she can spare us a few hours to help raise funds for our school's riding arena. It wouldn't cost her anything. She could sleep at my place and we'd feed her supper and breakfast."

"Just give the Ranchmen's plenty of advance notice," Harry Charles warned. "Her entourage would probably take every room upstairs."

Harry Charles took his little spiral-bound notebook from his shirt pocket and wrote on a page that he tore out and handed to Purvis. "Just send it to Belinda Stronach, MP at this address and don't bother buying a stamp. It's free postage."

"And let us know as soon as you get a reply," Perley said. "I think maybe we can make a few bucks on the side out of this."

"How so?" Purvis is always alert to money-making possibilities.

"Well, you know how in the big city bookstores they have those big boxes where they put Canadian books after a few months and sell them dirt cheap? I say we buy a few hundred of this one about Belinda and get her to autograph every one and then sell them at their original price."

"By gad, Perley," Harry Charles slapped him on the back. "By gad, it's a wonder you're not already driving a BMW."

"You know, that's a grand idea, Perley," Purvis gave him a back slap too. "Maybe I can get back all that money I spent on stamps on the letters I've been sending to Monte Solberg." He turned to Harry Charles. "I didn't know about this free letter thing. Cripes, I bet I've wasted at least 12 bucks."

Bouncing Hormonal Imbalance Act

"Purvis, you appear to be in a high dudgeon," Harry Charles remarked as Purvis slid his chair back and plunked himself into it with a grunt.

"It's a helluva lot better to be in one of those than in a brassiere," he replied. "Did you read this?" He flopped a raggedy copy of the Calgary Sun on the table. It was folded open to an inside page and one of the headlines read Men Growing Breasts. There were no photos accompanying the story, which I thought was unusual for the Sun.

Harry Charles picked it up and gave the story a scan and handed it over to Perley, who flipped over to the page with the horoscopes. When he was finished, he handed it to me and I flipped over to the page with the Sunshine Girl.

"Heard that on CHAT radio the other day," Harry Charles said. "Has to do with men and boys getting an overdose of hormones from shampoo."

"Looks to me," I said, "like this Sunshine Girl must use an awful lot of shampoo."

"Well, it's no concern to me," Perley said, "because I don't use shampoo. Never have, never will because it's too damned expensive."

"How do you keep what's left clean and shiny? Rainwater?"

"No, I use dish soap. I squirt a little from the kitchen into a bottle, fill it up with water and use that. Works pretty good over the rest of me, too."

Perley turned to me and asked what I use on the few wisps I

have remaining. I told them I use hotel shampoo, conditioner and body soaps.

"Haven't you guys seen his closet?" Harry Charles asked them. "He has one full closet, floor to ceiling, with shelves filled back to front with those tiny little bottles of bath stuff they have in hotel rooms. He has hundreds and hundreds of them, probably enough to last everybody in Manyberries for a lifetime."

"Wherever did you come across those?" Perley asked me.

"Well, you pick up a lot of stuff when you travel and I accumulated a ton of those during the 15 years I was on the road. Haven't paid for shampoo or soap for years."

"That's not all," Harry Charles told them, "he does the same as Perley: waters the stuff down so one small bottle lasts a month, assuming he showers at least once a week."

"What shampoo do you use, Purvis?"

"Whatever my wife uses, I think it's called Panties. I use her conditioner, too. But I'm not going to anymore; I'm going to find something else." He turned to Harry Charles. "You still have a full head of hair and I've seen you in a golf shirt, what do you use?"

"Whatever bar of soap is in my hand at the time. Nothing growing on this old carcass that isn't supposed to grow."

"I don't know why, but all this reminds me of Seinfeld," I said.

"Who's Seinfeld," Purvis asked.

"It's a television show, a comedy, and on one of their episodes they were promoting the idea of brassieres for men. I think they were calling it the Bro-Bra."

"I thought you didn't watch television."

"I don't, but I did when I was on the road. There wasn't a whole lot to do in a hotel at night except watch television, or read the Gideon Bible."

"Is that the program where a gang of young men and women hang around an apartment or a coffee joint and talk a lot?" Perley has satellite and claims he only watches news and public affairs programs.

"No, that was Friends."

"Is it the one where a married guy has his own television program about fixing up things around the house?" Purvis watches television when he's asked to mind his grandchildren at his sons' houses.

"No, as I recall that was Home Improvement but I wouldn't bet money on it."

"Well, what about this brassiere for men? Did it sell?"

"Geez, I don't know. I was probably half asleep when I saw it and it was a long time ago. It was just an observation that there are some similarities here between that and this hormone thing from shampoo. Sorry I raised it"

"To get back on topic, it's a terrible thing if men have to start wearing brassieres because they were persuaded it was important to have squeaky-clean and shiny hair." Harry Charles is vastly entertained by Purvis and always steers the conversation back to him when he's on a rant. "Where do you think we should go with this, Purvis?"

"Well, I think somebody should sue somebody," Purvis said. "You've got a whole world full of men running around with boobies just because they used their mothers' or sisters' or even wives' shampoo. They should put warning labels on those bottles."

"I think a whole world is stretching it a bit, but why not a class action suit against the shampoo companies?" Harry Charles asked. "You could argue that men have been hormonally unbalanced because of the shampoo companies' reckless disregard for their physical well-being in the pursuit of obscene profits."

"On the other hand, you could have women like this Sunshine Girl going to court as witnesses for the defence." I held up the paper so they could see her.

Harry Charles gave a low whistle. "By the looks of her, she not only uses it but probably drinks it too."

"But if you go to court, how many men are going to stand up before a judge and yank their shirts up to prove they've grown breasts? And how do you separate those who got them from shampoo and those who got them naturally from advancing years and gravity?" Perley took a swallow of his beer. "Seems to me there are only two of us here at this table who shouldn't be wearing golf shirts and it isn't Harry Charles and me."

"I'd worry about something else," Harry Charles told Purvis. "If you did get to court and a bunch of guys swore up and down that the shampoo had increased their breast size, wouldn't it be natural for people to start wondering if the same hormonal imbalance didn't create shrinkage somewhere else? Not many men would want people wondering if what they gained had been offset by the loss of something else."

"Well, you were the one who suggested we should go to court and sue their pants off," Purvis grumbled and turned to me. "They probably made that television show in Toronto, right?"

"No, it was actually made in Los Angeles but they pretended it was New York."

"Well, they're all the same in those cities. Probably a lot of guys there who use shampoo for that reason alone. But you're right, apart from guys like that, where would you find men who'd pull their shirts up in front of a judge? And even fewer if they thought people, especially women, were wondering about that other problem."

We all took a disappointed sip, knowing that Purvis was not going to pursue his legal action.

"But you know, if there are a lot of men wandering around who can't wear golf shirts because they used shampoo, there might be an opportunity here for a guy who's willing to invest in something to help them. What did you call it, a Bro-Bra? I don't think that's the name I'd choose."

"You thinking about going into the men's brassiere business, Purvis?" Harry Charles was leaning forward in pretend excitement.

"I can see in my mind's eye something that might have possibilities. Do you guys know what a bandeau is? How about a bandeau for men? But we wouldn't call it that. There'd be no reference to brassieres at all."

"I'm reminded of another television show," I said, "about a bunch of California lifeguards. They always opened that show with a shot of women lifeguards running toward the camera in slow motion. You could have a group of guys in golf shirts running at the camera in slow motion and then do it again but the second time they'd be wearing your apparatus."

"I'll keep that in mind once we get through product and prototype development and a copyright trademark name."

"I think" Harry Charles said, "naming the thing is going to be tricky. There's no way most men will wear anything with a name that makes people think about brassieres."

"I'm already ahead of you on that." Purvis took his little spiral-bound notebook from his pocket. "We'll come out with an elastic thing that we'll call the Man-Flattener. We'll advertise them as being available only in stores where quality golf shirts are sold."

Charlie's New Car

Charlie was a dog of questionable ancestry. A short black mutt, he'd been part of our family for a lot of years. Some people whom he accepted as friends opined that one of his parents might have been a Labrador and the other a Border Collie. Others, who knew dogs, suggested that if either of those breeds were in his family, it was several generations back and more recent generations might have included either a Vietnamese dwarf pig or a breed of dog as yet unknown to any of the Kennel Clubs or specific breed clubs that litter the planet.

Charlie and Harry Charles were best friends. I once took a photo of Charlie and just as I snapped it, he narrowed his eyes and stuck out his tongue. I showed it to Harry Charles and he liked it so much he got it blown up and framed and hung it in the kitchen. Whenever he had visitors he invented different scenarios for the photo. One time it was taken on the night when Pierre Trudeau was re-elected. Other times it was snapped when Charlie was watching television and Kim Campbell won the leadership of the old Progressive Conservative party; when Ralph Klein became Premier of Alberta; and when Bob Rae was elected Premier in Ontario.

Around Manyberries, Charlie was known as a dog that had a connoisseur's nose for cow manure. Charlie could find cow manure even when it was petrified by 30 below January temperatures. And he would roll in it as enthusiastically in January as he would have when it first hit the ground on a hot July day.

As Harry Charles often said, "for Charlie, those cow flops are like Chanel Number Five is for a woman except for Charlie, it's Corral Number Five."

Truth is, Charlie would take his roll and then strut around town like he was God's gift to humankind. Come to think of it, even when he wasn't covered in his favourite scent, he strutted about like he owned the town and every other mongrel in it. Charlie would walk a mile from town on hot summer days looking for his favourite cologne and when he returned, if he managed to sneak in the back door of the Ranchmen's Saloon, he could clear that place in minutes. It wasn't as if those people were unused to the scent he preferred but it was the intensity of it that got them. You could never get too much of a good thing as far as Charlie was concerned and as I said earlier, Charlie had a talented nose for searching out only the best.

Well, that's just a little backgrounder on Charlie's olfactory senses to set the scene for Charlie's adventure with the new car.

It was a brand new Renault station wagon that Harry Charles said came all the way from France.

Now, around Manyberries, there are some who might remark that anything built and driven in France wouldn't last long on these prairie gravel roads, or even just sitting parked outside the Ranchmen's. If they had known the meaning of the word effeminate they would have called it that and spit tobacco juice in its general direction. I have to say that nobody can spit tobacco juice in the general direction of something in a more dismissive way than the folks in Manyberries.

One September Harry Charles asked me if I wanted to go hunting partridge and said we could take Charlie along to see if he had taken any interest in hunting. We would go in the Renault and Charlie could have the whole rear section to himself so he could bark at will at every fencepost we passed or at cows for a little variety.

The next morning found us out along an abandoned railway heavily weeded over and flanked on both sides by fields of wheat stubble.

Charlie, ever anxious to explore new bushes on which to leave his mark and to find new cow flops, got out a little ahead of us and I had to call him back to heel. He obeyed for a few steps and then got out ahead again. After about the seventh time, when he tried to sneak out ahead, I tapped him on the head lightly with my shotgun barrel.

It wasn't that he was trying to hunt birds because Charlie had no interest in hunting. He just liked being out there looking for bushes to wet down or things to roll in. And if he got too far ahead of us, there was a chance he'd spook the birds before we got within shooting range.

That tap on the head didn't hurt him but it certainly bruised his pride because he turned right around and headed back to the

And God Created Manyberries

Renault. We turned to watch him go and he looked back to see if we were watching and then gave us the bird with a flip of his curly tail and just kept on going.

We had a successful walk and headed on back to the Renault with a half dozen partridges in the bag. When we got to the bottom of the rise where the vehicle was parked I whistled to let Charlie know we were returning but he didn't respond. Harry Charles said he guessed Charlie was still sulking from the tap on the head.

When we topped the rise, we could see why Charlie hadn't come running down to meet us. He was sitting up on the roof of the Renault surveying the kingdom around him. He did give us a few wags and then slid down the windshield and across the hood of the wagon and jumped to the ground.

"My new car," groaned Harry Charles, "a brand new car without a scratch and that gawdamned dog has run his toenails all over it."

I was embarrassed because Charlie was my dog and I didn't have enough money to pay for fixing all the toenail scratches that ran in both directions from the hood ornament right up to the windshield and on the roof as well. About all I could do was hope that Harry Charles' affection for Charlie would trump his anguish over the scratches.

Well, it was a bit strained and quiet as we cleaned the birds and sipped the brandy-fortified tea I had brought along. When the birds were clean, Harry Charles called Charlie over to let him sniff the dead birds. "Might as well give him a whiff and hope that it encourages him to want to hunt," he said.

Trouble was Charlie took one sniff of the birds and of the offal and promptly got sick to his stomach.

Back at the Ranchmen's where we stopped for the traditional tot of Wood's Black Navy rum and a pitcher of beer, Harry Charles was lamenting to one and all about the damage done to the paint on his Renault. Most of the other regulars looked at each other and nodded that they'd been right all along – no way some little French car could stand up to the hardships of the prairies.

Then all of a sudden, Harry Charles started to laugh. "Damndest thing," he said, "here's Charlie, who can roll in the ripest cow manure and strut about like he was some sort of runt version of Rin Tin Tin from Hollywood. He can clear this place any hot July day when he finds a good ripe patty but when he sniffs a little pile of guts and a few partridge, he loses his biscuits. I think what we should do is nominate Charlie for political office."

A few of the boys wondered why a weak stomach would make a good politician and Harry Charles explained.

"It's because Charlie's already a politician. He can roll in that other stuff every day when nobody's watching but get him into something he thinks is bad when there are witnesses and he folds like cheap chair in a church basement."

Looking back I am grateful that Charlie lost control of his stomach before we were in the Renault and headed back to Manyberries. I think if that had happened in the back seat of Harry Charles' new Renault it would have taken the rest of the hunting season for the old guy to get over his mad on at Charlie.

He and Harry Charles remained close friends and HC always called on Charlie to go hunting even if I was busy. They shared a fondness for cheese and onion sandwiches and those miniature chocolate bars you buy by the bagful at Halloween.

I do not recommend this diet to dog owners because veterinarians have warned that onions and chocolate are toxic to dogs. Charlie lived to the ripe old age of $19 \times 7 = 136$ human years but I would not credit his preferred hunting lunches for that accomplishment.

I think the real reason for his longevity was the fresh cow manure.

The Flying Gourmets

Purvis was looking quite anxious and indignant when he walked into the Ranchmen's and plunked himself down at our table. It's only when he's anxious and indignant that he plunks himself because he has a tender back and usually just eases down onto the chair.

"My cousin in Saskatoon told me that Stephen Harper is eating pork when he flies on the government jet. What the hell is the matter with him, him being an Alberta boy and all? Not that I have anything against pork but what does that say about our beef industry?"

"He eats beef too, when he flies. At least it's on the menu," Harry Charles said, "along with salmon."

"That's not what Arnie said. He said the Star Phoenix reported that the catering contract calls for roast tenderloin of pork."

"As I recall, Arnie votes NDP and he's probably twisting the story a little to get a rise out of you. Fact is the story said the caterers are to supply roast tenderloin of pork with sautéed mushroom sauce, grilled salmon steak with lemon butter and filet mignon with sautéed mushrooms."Nobody ever disputes Harry Charles because of all the newspapers that he reads.

"Well, Arnie has been in a snit since the Conservatives won the election, and he does like to put them in a bad light," Purvis conceded. "I don't like it when people are so partisan they exaggerate to score points against their political adversaries, or get petty in their criticism."

"You were watching one of those political shows from Ottawa on television last night, weren't you," Harry Charles said.

"Yes, well, I was at my son's place looking after the grandchildren while they went over to Taber so I decided to see what's happening politically. Why do you ask?"

"That's been the story of the day for a whole week now, ever since those pontificators in the media formulated their collective opinion. It's that left-leaning groupthink bunch again. They all bathe in the same tub and then drink the water when they're clean." Harry Charles likes sheep and loves to see them in the field but not in the media.

"But Purvis, at least you were articulate in expressing your opinion."

"Geez," I said, "I'd love to fly in one of those things and have a menu like that on offer. Except for the salmon with lemon butter because of my cholesterol. I'd have to pass on the butter. It'd beat the hell out of cheese and onion sandwiches and beer on our hunting trips."

"Nothing beats cheese and onion sandwiches and a cold beer when you're hunting, or any time for that matter," Perley said. "That's what I had for lunch today."

"I can tell and you went heavier on the onion than the cheese, didn't you?"

"Well, I'd argue that Stephen should only have beef on the menu to promote the industry," Purvis said. "And I wouldn't mind if he had beef from all the provinces, even Newfoundland."

"They wouldn't sell him beef from Newfoundland," Harry Charles said. "They need that cow for the milk."

"You know, it's too bad they have to have that civilized junk instead of venison, or pheasant, or maybe even a good pike steak," Perley said. "I was thinking maybe we should pull together some stuff from our freezers and send it off to him in one those freeze-dried containers."

Turning to me he added: "You could toss in some of those venison sausages and smokies you got done up at Ryan's in Calgary. We had one of those big garlic ones for supper last night and there was enough for two of us."

"You know, you're on to something, Perley." Purvis leaned over and drew an X in the beer on the table with his finger. "That would put Manyberries on the map if we could supply the meat for the government jet." He leaned back and stuck a hand in the air to let Hazel know it was time for a refill.

"Harry Charles, you probably still have a lot of mallards and pheasants in your freezer. I've got a ton of elk from two years ago. The grandkids are refusing to eat any more of that moose my son got last year so there's plenty of that. And I know Perley still has a lot of partridge put away."

"I admire your civic spirit and initiative, Purvis." Harry Charles is always, always willing to nudge Purvis along when he starts getting enthusiastic about a new idea or project. "But it'd have to be clear that it's all being donated or we'll wind up in jail for selling wild game."

"Of course we'll donate it," Perley said, "providing they put on the menu that those supplies for the flying meals are courtesy of Manyberries, Alberta."

"It goes without saying, I trust, that if the Liberals ever win again, the whole deal is off." I wanted to make sure we all had a clear understanding on this point.

"Absolutely, there's no way I'd be supplying them," Purvis assured me. "The way those guys go at the trough we'd have to be out every year after moose." And he said that without any partisan political exaggeration or pettiness.

"Excellent idea, Purvis. So you'll write to Stephen and offer our services as the meat suppliers for the Challenger menu?" Harry Charles was being as encouraging as possible because he knew Purvis would ask for help in writing the letter. He also knows that all letters, except the crank mail, get answered. When it came, Stephen's reply would be framed for posterity and hung on the wall of the Ranchmen's. He'd insist on that in exchange for his assistance in composing the letter of offer. Purvis would agree because his name and that of the Prime Minister would be on the same page.

Well, this all got started last March and we're still awaiting a reply from Prime Minister Harper.

He'd better respond soon if he intends to accept our offer because there isn't a whole lot of wild game left in our freezers and the moose meat Purvis got from his son is getting freezer burned, which means it's only good for stew.

Cultivating Corruption

As I recall it was Purvis who said he'd heard on the radio that corruption was rampant in Ottawa and that people there were even beginning to acknowledge it. Not all of the people, he reported, but the radio said that at least some had become aware of it.

That certainly got the Ranchmen's buzzing that night because the consensus for years has been that nobody in Ottawa was ever aware of anything.

Purvis, who harbours political aspirations, thought that maybe this could be a seminal event for Manyberries: "A chance to examine our own attitudes and behaviour so that we'll never stand accused of ignoring a culture of corruption and entitlement like they do in Ottawa."

"Geez, I don't know about this," I said, "I wouldn't even know where to begin."

"You see, that's the problem," Purvis said, "we're so wilfully ignorant we don't even know of the existence of corruption within our midst."

"You're not thinking of investigating Perley, are you?" I asked. Perley is our recently re-mandated Postmaster Sort-Of and Postman Sort-Of after beating Purvis handily in a general election for the job he personally created. Perley doesn't get a federal paycheque for the work he does with the mail because Ottawa has no knowledge of our arrangement with him. As I said, the consensus in Manyberries is that Ottawa never has any knowledge of anything important.

"No, and I'd be the first to defend Perley against any such accusations," Purvis replied.

Purvis was so soundly defeated by Perley that he knew the political career he might aspire to would be forever crushed if he crossed paths with Perley on any issue. You just don't pick fights with people of huge influence in a community.

And God Created Manyberries

"No, I'm talking about real corruption, the kind that ordinary people go to jail for, or get rich from if they're in business or politics," he continued.

"Well," I said with what I felt was admirable subtlety, "it wasn't that long ago that some kid sold me a gas tank cap that fit my Suburban for five bucks after I lost the original one. It struck me as strange that the key on my ring fit that gas cap. It would have been pretty corrupt if what he did was sell me my own gas cap back after he stole it."

"That's peanuts compared to what I'm talking about here," Purvis said.

The kid I mentioned is a nephew of Purvis and does chores for him from time to time. I concluded that was one area of potential corruption that would never see the light of day before a public inquiry if Purvis appointed one.

"No," Purvis continued, "I mean real rotten corruption, like the stuff they're talking about on the radio. It'd put Manyberries on the world map if we got something like that going. And if we got federal money to hold the inquiry, we could get big city lawyers here by the dozen and that'd be good for business." Purvis always lights up when he thinks about getting free government money.

Hazel put the mugs on the table and said she had one major area of concern. "When that dog of your does his business outside your yard, Purvis, the whole town gets corrupted if the wind's blowing the wrong way." Purvis' dog is Three-Eyed Tom, the biggest dog anybody ever saw.

"Not only that," Hazel continued, "when he does his business in somebody else's yard, they have to call in a backhoe and half-ton because you just can't stoop and scoop after your dog, Purvis."

Purvis was flummoxed, to repeat what Harry Charles observed. He couldn't very well call a public inquiry into the toiletry habits of his own dog and if he did, how many big city lawyers would touch a case like that? There probably isn't a politician living who'd walk anywhere near something that scandalous. In Manyberries, mothers keep their kids in the house after Three-Eyed Tom visits, if he visits to do his business. They are kept in the house until the old man comes home from work or the Ranchmen's and gets to work with the heavy excavating tools.

Purvis' aspiring political career was headed south before it had even gone one inch north.

He ordered two pickled oeufs from the big jar on the bar and took a thoughtful bite of one.

"We could, I suppose, advertise widely that Manyberries is

incorruptible," he said, wiping a bit of egg white that stuck to the stubble on his upper lip. "We could call ourselves the town that can't be bought."

"That's as good a slogan as any," Harry Charles said, "but truth be known, Purvis, there isn't anybody in town who wouldn't sell the house or property if some sucker ever came along and offered a higher-than-market bid. Why, I'd wager you'd even sell Three-Eyed Tom if some circus owner made you a big enough offer."

"I wouldn't take less than $800 for Tom," Purvis replied, "but I might let him go for less if my back gets any worse and he does too much of his business at home and not in somebody else's yard."

Dog Daze in Manyberries

Harry Charles was fuming when he came into the Ranchmen's and you could tell it by the way he tossed the Calgary Herald on the table and muttered about a terrible waste of trees and ink.

"The media is the biggest waste of a man's time there ever was and that includes going to churches where the preachers preach politics instead of fire and brimstone."

I picked up the front section to see what had him boiling. There was a big story about Peter MacKay and Belinda Stronach. The story claimed that MacKay allegedly likened Stronach to a dog during a debate in the House of Commons. There was more stuff on it in the inside pages.

"Is it this stuff about MacKay and Stronach?" I asked. "I imagine a lot of people would find that fascinating. The same people who read those tabloids about movie stars and what's her name, Paris Hilton, and space invaders."

"Don't get me started on Paris Hilton," he said. "Any time I see a picture of her or a headline with her name in it, I rip it out of the newspaper so it can't be read."

"There must be a lot of holes in those newspapers you have stacked up at home," Perley offered. "I mean the ones you already haven't scissored apart and filed away." Harry Charles has a vast filing system of newspaper clippings that he keeps up to date, and he can generally find information on just about any topic or issue you can imagine. It comes in handy when we have political debates and can't agree on what might have been said by some politician or even when. He has a medicare file at least three feet deep going back to the 1960s when politicians of all stripes were promising to provide health care absolutely free to every Canadian, dead, living or yet to be born.

Harry Charles took a gulp from his mug and wiped the foam from his upper lip. "It's the waste of ink, paper and my time that riles me," he said. "I read the damn story to the finish looking for the point of it, and there is no point."

"What would you have them write about, if not this?" I asked. "Could be a lot of people with dogs would find that interesting. Remember when MacKay and Belinda broke up over her joining the Liberals and all the women thought he looked cute in his sorrow wandering around his farm with that mutt he borrowed?"

"I'd like to have seen this much coverage over that clean air legislation the government brought in," Harry Charles answered. "All I got was the other parties calling it bad and that sure as hell doesn't help me make a decision on my investments. You know, should I dump my shares in the oil sands and buy shares in windmill companies?"

"I think the point of the story is Peter was wrong to say that Belinda reminds him of a dog," Purvis offered. "If that's what he said, and it says here he says he didn't say it." Purvis has made it abundantly clear that if he were 30, well maybe 40 years younger and not married and was living anywhere near Ottawa, he'd have what they call the hots for Belinda. The rest of us aren't so convinced. After Belinda jumped ship to the Liberals, Harry Charles and Perley likened her to Paris Hilton, and considering what they think of Paris that was pretty cruel to Belinda.

"What irritates me is all the newspapers yet to come, knowing that for at least a week that's all the news we'll get from Ottawa. It'll be Belinda this and Peter that until my stomach gets riled. I'd wager there's nothing on earth lazier than those reporters in Ottawa, not even cats. Why, even some cats have half a brain and contribute by chasing mice."

"Well, if that's what sells newspapers, that means that's what the people want, so they're only doing what the public wants," Perley said. "I'll take your word for it on the lazy part."

"If he did say she looked like a dog, I hope he didn't have a picture of a dog like Charlie in his mind," I said.

Harry Charles chuckled. "Charlie would be growling if he heard somebody say he looked like Belinda Stronach. He's a dog of no small pride."

"Well, what are you going to do, stop reading newspapers for a week until those lazy louts in Ottawa get tired of writing about dogs?" Perley waved at the bar for another round. "Geez, you'll have stacks of unread newspapers all over the place." Harry Charles is very diligent about reading all his newspapers, from front to back.

And God Created Manyberries

"No, I'll just do the Paris Hilton thing and tear out those stories and toss them in the garbage so I won't be tempted to read them. Maybe I'll write a few letters to editors and tell them they should try to hire people in Ottawa who can write about important stuff."

"I'll make a deal with you," Purvis offered. "If you scissor out those stories, you can give them to me. I can put them in my Belinda scrapbook that I'm saving to show her if she ever comes to town." Purvis has it in mind to invite Belinda to Manyberries to help raise funds for the next big civic project we undertake. There's a public outhouse behind the Ranchmen's that needs a little refurbishing and, from time to time, it arises as an issue for potential future consideration.

"Now you've just conjured a scary thought," Harry Charles told Purvis. "What would you get if you put together a scrapbook of Belinda stories and another on something important like the environment and then measured the thickness of each?"

Nobody offered an answer.

Ageism in Manyberries

Old Rutherford came into the Ranchmen's much earlier than usual, about two hours before what people who think they're civilized and sophisticated would call the cocktail hour. At the Ranchmen's our cocktail hour begins when more than two of us are at the table, ready to debrief on the day's weather and tomorrow's forecast. Generally speaking that's sometime between 4:30 and 6:00. It ends abruptly for each individual at five minutes before supper is to be laid on the table in their respective kitchens. For Harry Charles that means five to six; for Purvis, 10 past six and for Perley 25 past six. It takes no more than five minutes to walk to any home in Manyberries from the Ranchmen's so it should be obvious to even the most casual observer the exact time the plates hit the table in various homes. Personally, I like the hamburgers at the Ranchmen's and more often than not forego the long walk home. I like them so much that there are days when my cocktail hour begins just before noon when they fire up the grill for lunch.

Old Rutherford was obviously there that afternoon on a mission because he came straight over to the table we occupy instead of the one he normally favours over in the dark corner beside the table where Four-Eyed Tom does his crossword puzzles. As in any quality lounge during cocktail hour, at the Ranchmen's it is customary to wave a new arrival to an empty chair and push across an untouched mug of beer to him to help him get started. It is the custom then for the newcomer to hold up a minimum of four fingers: one to signal a replacement for the mug offered, two for himself and the fourth finger for another mug for whomever at the table finishes first or for somebody who might arrive within the next few minutes. Old Rutherford does not buy into that custom because, to put it kindly, he's cheap.

And God Created Manyberries

I was enjoying a glass of red wine and because there was only one glass on the table, it was safe for Old Rutherford to sit down. He knew I wasn't going to let him sip from my glass.

"The Mrs and I think that you are prematurely old for your age," he informed me, "and we think that a change in your philosophy might give you a more youthful outlook on life."

I ran my hand over what's left of my hair, wondering if I was about to get a sales job on the hormonal benefits of year-round sun tanning. Old Rutherford and the Mrs spend countless hours in the sun, gathering sunshine as they call it. He has a full head of hair, which you don't often see on men his age. I'm not sure how old Old Rutherford is but Purvis and Perley say they think he probably fought in the Boer War. Harry Charles just snorts that Old Rutherford is even older than that and probably *started* the Boer War.

While I'm on this subject, however, I should point out that we never call him "Old" Rutherford to his face because we read somewhere that Ottawa frowns on ageism almost as much as it does on all the other isms.

"It's the dry climate and too much time spent in the sun," I said. "It wears out a guy's skin and tightens it so hair can't grow through it."

"Where did you read that, in Playboy?" he asked.

"No, it's a theory of mine that just only came to mind."

"This has nothing to do with your physical appearance," he said, "although you could, with some effort, do something about that. This is about your belief that tan lines are appealing."

"Whenever in hell did I say that?"

"Purvis told me you said tan lines on women are appealing and you were conditioned at an early age to think so because of the photos in Playboy magazine."

"I don't remember that. Although I will admit that I think tan lines are sexy and I do remember that years ago the women in Playboy had them."

"It was when you were discussing the tanning salon the Mrs and I purchased and set up in our old trailer."

It dawned on me then and I remembered a conversation about the tanning salon. I could only recall that it was late in the cocktail hour, or even later, when we had had that conversation.

"No, the simple fact is you are wrong." Old Rutherford was nothing if not insistent. "As I just finished telling you, a shift in your philosophy might give you a more youthful outlook on life."

"What do you propose, Mr. Rutherford: that I scrap my collection of mint condition Playboy magazines up to the year tan lines disappeared?"

"No, we just think you should read and ponder this," and he handed over a full front page from a back section of a recent Calgary Herald. He pointed at a couple of boxes on the bottom of the page with the headlines Top 10 Turn-Ons and Turn-Offs for Women and Men. He pointed a brown and leathery finger at Number Nine for men and Number Eight for women under the Turn-Off lists. It said tan lines were Turn-Offs for both sexes, although that's pretty far down the list of the Top 10.

"We've seen you sun tanning in your backyard," he said, "and you're always wearing shorts. You probably do that because up until now you believed that women would find your tan line appealing."

"No, that's not it at all. I wear shorts because I don't want somebody accusing me of indecent exposure and because if I'm going to sit in the sun to get a tan, I want to be able to see, in the privacy of my own mirror, that sitting there doing nothing produced some result, even if it's only a tan line."

"You should read what Freud said about human behaviour," he informed me. "Nobody does anything without regard to the impact it will have on the opposite sex."

"Well, you've certainly given me food for thought. I'll keep this and read it carefully and try to absorb as much of it as I can." I held up a hand with two fingers extended to signal Hazel to bring two mugs over for Old Rutherford, but he declined, saying he had another engagement and couldn't stay. He stood and walked over to his usual table in the corner and signalled Hazel to bring him two.

I knew he'd be watching so I removed my trifocals and bent over to read the newspaper.

Leading the list of Turn-Offs for both men and women was baby talk and I nodded my head in agreement. Sweat was also on both lists and I couldn't have agreed more. I go out of my way to avoid anything that might create sweat, like gardening or other manual labour. I don't much care for sarcasm either and decided to tell Harry Charles he should tone it down because women find it a Turn-Off. I've never had any interest in getting anything pierced because it would hurt so I wouldn't be turning women off in that regard. Same with tattoos. I don't know precisely what a brainiac is but I know I'm not one so again I'm on safe ground. Long hair turns off women so that's home run territory for me.

All in all it was a very interesting article. I was still pondering it when Purvis, Perley and Harry Charles walked in and settled down for the cocktail hour and held up over a dozen fingers among them to tell Hazel how many mugs they wanted to get the hour started.

When she arrived at our table I asked her to take a mug over to Old

Rutherford who was sitting alone for whatever previous engagement he had scheduled. "Tell him thanks for me and that I appreciate his enlightening me and that I will give it a thorough read tonight."

"What did he give you to read? Harry Charles asked, "A book on why the sun will never set on the British Empire?"

"It'd be an old book," Perley said. "The sun set on the empire when they elected their first Labour government."

"No, it was when they got rid of Margaret Thatcher," Purvis argued. "Or maybe it was when Winston Churchill died."

"Are you guys being sarcastic?" I asked. "Because if you are, you should know that women find that a Turn-Off."

Belinda Goes Home

"Have you been hanging out at Old Rutherford's tanning trailer?" Harry Charles asked me as I eased into my chair at the Ranchmen's.

"No, I just got back last night."

"Where've you been?"

"Palm Springs."

"We wondered where you were last night, in fact somebody asked why you weren't here."

"Last night? Cripes, I've been gone for a whole month."

"So I guess you haven't heard the latest news?"

"Not unless it's about diets, movie stars, the desert, golf or American politics. All I had to read down there was the Desert Sun and all there was to watch was Katie Couric and hours of stuff about Rosie O'Donnell, who quit some television program after she had an argument with Donald Trump. They don't go in much for Canadian news down there, although the Desert Sun carries a weekly summary of Canadian stuff, including the lottery numbers and I'm not a millionaire again."

"Anyway, the big news is the Conservatives have revealed their environmental program to fight greenhouse gas emissions and global warming."

"So who's protesting and screaming about it?"

"Everybody. The New Democrats, Bloc Quebecois, Green Party, tree huggers, industry, all those environmental groups, probably David Suzuki, Liberals and anybody else who can walk and chew gum."

"So it must be a good plan," I said. "What do you think about it?"

"Can't say just yet. I'm waiting for the whole package to be delivered from Ottawa. But based on the superficial summaries I've read in the newspapers and the even less that I got from television and radio, I'm optimistic."

It was then that Purvis and Perley arrived and settled into their chairs.

"Where were you?" Purvis asked. "Somebody asked when you didn't show up last night."

"Last night? Cripes, as I told Harry Charles, I've been in Palm Springs. For a month."

"So I guess you haven't heard the latest news. Or has Harry Charles already told you?"

"Yeah, he was just telling me about it."

"I think it's a big loss for Canada," Purvis said. "Although she does say that she's not withdrawing from public life, just going to focus on other things."

"Are you talking about that, uhh, Rosie O'Donnell?"

"Rose O' who? No, I'm talking about Belinda leaving politics and going back to work for her daddy."

I might have mentioned previously that Purvis has what they used to call the hots for Belinda. If he was 20, well 30 years younger, he might even finagle a way to get to Ottawa in the hopes she'd have dinner and maybe, in his dreams, breakfast with him.

"No, the Desert Sun isn't like Canadian newspapers, which is why I like it. They wouldn't waste ink on a story like Belinda."

"Well, whatever," Purvis shook his head. He can't understand why Harry Charles, Perley and I don't share his enthusiasm for all things Belinda.

"But the good news is, Purvis, she's going to, according to the Calgary Sun, dedicate increasingly more time to humanitarian issues as well as manage her old man's jillion dollar empire. Jillion is my word, not the Sun's." Harry Charles is scrupulous about getting his quotes right.

"Still, I wonder why she's quitting politics. Hell, she could have run for the Liberal leadership next year when that Dion guy folds."

"Purvis, that's a cruel thing to say even if they are Liberals, that they might seriously consider choosing her to lead them. Geez, if she won, I'd bet a lot of Liberals would head for foreign hills. I would too, if she ever got within sniffing distance of the Prime Minister's office." Harry Charles got a nod of approval from Perley and me.

Purvis stood suddenly, saying he had to go home for a few minutes. "Tell Hazel to leave my beer alone and that I'll be back for another."

"Wonder why he had to leave so quickly?" I said.

"Probably going home to see if he has any shares in Belinda's daddy's company," Perley offered. "If not, he'll probably call his broker up in Calgary tomorrow and tell him to buy some."

"But you know, if I had shares in pulp and paper companies, I'd be a little worried. I should tell Purvis when he gets back."

"Why is that?" I asked, figuring Harry Charles would have something to make Purvis even more fretful.

"Well, look at it this way. When Belinda leaves politics, the newspapers can reduce the space they use for what passes as news from Ottawa. That means they'll need less paper. That means lower profits for pulp and paper and that in turn lowers dividends and share prices."

"Purvis won't have time to finish the beer he left, let alone order a new one if you tell him as soon as he returns," Perley said.

"Well, he gained a few pounds over the winter so the decline in consumption added to the exercise and worry might be a remedy he'd welcome."

When Purvis returned, he offered us some financial investing wisdom. "Investors have a responsibility to themselves always to be on top of their investments. You have to read everything the companies send you, everything the market analysts are saying and you have to attend every annual shareholders' meeting." I don't think he saw Perley wink at Harry Charles and me.

"Well, I don't have any shares in any businesses," Perley said. "But I'm wondering, now that Belinda is going and Paris Hilton is in jail, it won't be just the paper and ink companies that'll be bankrupt. What'll they use to fill the television programs?"

Harry Charles then explained his investment theory to Purvis but he didn't react as we expected.

"Won't hurt me," he said, "I never invest in anything I don't use myself. And since I stopped reading newspapers, the only shares I own in a company in the paper business are for an outfit that sells toilet tissue."

And God Created Manyberries

Retiring in Manyberries

Old Rutherford walked into the Ranchmen's and dragged a chair over to our table and sat down with me, Purvis, Perley, Harry Charles and Four-Eyed Tom. We knew something big was in the wind because Old Rutherford wasn't accompanied by the Mrs and looked a bit out of breath. That, plus the fact that Old Rutherford came from England and considers us as mere colonials and always heads to his own table of choice, told us that something was out of the ordinary.

"The young woman who talks the news on CHAT said an hour ago that Ralph is retiring and young Preston is thinking about going after his job," he informed us.

"Ralph who?" Perley wondered.

"Ralph Klein." Old Rutherford was as exasperated as only Old Rutherford can be when talking to dirt-on-their-boots colonials.

I should add that Old Rutherford came as an orphan and was placed with a farmer in Saskatchewan who allowed him to sleep in the barn and eat breakfast in exchange for all the work an eight-year-old was capable of doing. Old Rutherford was granted permission to keep his name because the farmer wanted to make sure that there'd be no confusion when it came time for his own sons to claim their legal inheritance. That farmer was a founding member of one of Canada's progressive and socially conscious political parties.

Old Rutherford developed an unhealthy disrespect for all things Canadian out of that experience and that includes Canadians, with the exception of the Mrs, whom he met and married in Moose Jaw.

"What's he retiring from?" Harry Charles wondered.

"From the Premiership of the province. Don't you men follow current events? Don't you know that Ralph Klein is Premier?"

"Guess maybe we'd heard that," Purvis conceded, "but for the life of me I can't recall him ever visiting Manyberries."

If there's one thing Old Rutherford is short on it's patience and if or when he practises it, it has never been in the company of those of us sitting at the table.

"I suppose the next thing you'll ask is who is Preston," he said.

"Preston who?" Harry Charles was always willing to oblige anyone, even Old Rutherford.

"Preston Manning, the son of Ernest, the longest-serving Premier this province ever had."

"You know, that reminds me of an old argument we used to have here back when Peter Lougheed was Premier," Perley said. He turned to Harry Charles. "You remember when people used to give Lougheed credit for all the money we had back then from crude oil and natural gas?"

"Yep, I remember that," Harry Charles said. "In fact, there were some who said it was a toss-up whether it was God or Lougheed who put the gas and oil under the ground."

"Sure, I remember that." Purvis chimed in. "There were those who worshipped Lougheed and said if it weren't for him we'd still be kicking horse buns down the street for excitement instead of driving to Taber to play the VLT machines."

"As I recall it was some guy on the radio who knew a little about our history who finally set it straight," Perley said, turning to Old Rutherford. "He said it was not Lougheed who put the oil and gas underground and he had proof. All the others who argued that it was God were wrong too."

"I've never heard about that," Old Rutherford said. "Of course it wasn't Lougheed who gave us our crude oil and natural gas resources. That would have been, for lack of a better word, the work of God."

"Nope, this guy on the radio had it right," Harry Charles told Old Rutherford. "You didn't come here until long after we did and you don't know the real history of Alberta whereas this radio guy obviously knew what he was talking about.

"You see, this radio guy's theory was that while God is all powerful, He isn't so all powerful that He can designate where crude oil and natural gas will be found. He argued there has only been one entity in history with that much power."

"Well if it wasn't God, and Lougheed certainly never made that claim, who did he credit with giving us all this wealth?" They now had Old Rutherford where they wanted him.

It came out as one voice from all four of them. I was sipping from my shot glass of black rum or I would have joined the chorus.

"Ernest Manning."

And God Created Manyberries

"You're telling me that people believe it was Ernest Manning who arranged to have the crude oil and natural gas in Alberta and not somewhere else in Canada?" Old Rutherford was making moves that he was preparing to depart, which I think was their plan all along.

"Yep, couldn't have been anybody other than old Ernest," Purvis confirmed. "You see, old Ernest had a radio program way back then and the way most folks saw it, radio was sort of God-like in its magic. If Ernest could talk straight at us through the radio and not even be in the next room, well, there wasn't anything he couldn't do."

"So, most folks just decided back then that Ernest used the radio to get the oil and gas here in Alberta." Perley and Harry Charles had told me this story a dozen times.

"All he did," Perley said, "was use his radio program to let God know Alberta needed that oil and gas. Do you think God is gonna argue with a guy who's got his own radio program?"

Old Rutherford left rather abruptly, shaking his head in despair or disgust, and we picked up on the conversation he had interrupted.

"If Preston decides he wants to be Premier, I'm gonna vote for him," Four-Eyed Tom declared.

"You know what we should have told Old Rutherford, more for his own edification than anything?" Harry Charles asked.

"We should have told him that it was Ernest Manning who invented medicare and not Tommy Douglas. That would have made his head spin."

"Problem with that is Old Rutherford's got in-laws in Moose Jaw. Last thing we need is to start a shooting war with that bunch over there." Purvis also has in-laws in Moose Jaw but they never discuss politics at family reunions.

"What we should do is write a letter to Ralph inviting him to retire in Manyberries," Harry Charles said. "We could send it from the Ranchmen's Preservation Society."

"There is no Ranchmen's Preservation Committee," Purvis interrupted.

"We could create one," Perley offered.

"And I suppose you mean this Ranchmen's?"

"Exactly. If Ralph retired here in Manyberries, that would absolutely guarantee the survival of the Ranchmen's even if the rest of us stopped coming, which isn't likely."

"We should write to CHAT and see if they'd be interested in hiring Ralph to say the news for them," Four-Eyed Tom suggested.

"But that's a good hour and a half commute and we need guys like Ralph close by," Purvis said. "I have another idea. Why not tell him he can be Mayor of Manyberries? He was Mayor of Calgary a few years back and with that experience he should be able to handle the chores here."

"We could set him up with a table here in the bar and get a small filing cabinet and let him go to work." Perley was getting enthused.

"It would spare him the time and trouble of leaving the office to go somewhere for lunch and that'd be an extra hour or two of survival time for the Ranchmen's."

"How much extra money do you think that would drag into Manyberries and the Ranchmen's with all those people coming here to see the former Premier of Alberta?" Purvis wondered.

"Not a penny, except for whatever Ralph spent," Harry Charles answered him.

"You think all those people coming here to visit a former Premier wouldn't spend money once they got here?" Four-Eyed was incredulous. "They're not gonna stop off and not eat, or have a drink, or maybe stop in next door and have a grilled cheese sandwich?"

"That's not the point," Harry Charles told him. "The point is nobody will come to visit. Who'd drive even halfway down the main street to see a retired politician? They're a dime a dozen, scattered all over from here to breakfast."

"Then why in God's name did you suggest we invent a committee to invite him to retire here?" Purvis was a bit disappointed because he had visions of hobnobbing with an important retired politician which might have furthered his own political ambitions.

"You boys don't think big picture, like politicians claim they do." Harry Charles paused and gave us a slow look and shook his head. "You forget that Ralph was Mayor of Calgary back when they had the Olympics there. You remember what that did for Calgary in dragging in the money?"

"There's no way, even with Ralph as our Mayor, that Manyberries would ever bid on the Olympics, let alone *win*, Purvis said and shook his head over Harry Charles' naiveté.

"You think big picture too much and not enough small picture, sort of like the politicians," Harry Charles said, giving Purvis a patient smile.

"What we do is get him here, appoint him Mayor and Chairman of the Olympics Bid Committee. He's a retired politician and misses all the attention and would probably issue a press release saying he has been appointed both Mayor and Chair, hoping it'd draw interest from the newspapers and he'd be back in the news."

"What good would that do?" Four-Eyed Tom was getting very confused. "Anybody reading that in a newspaper would say it was flat-out dumb and stupid."

And God Created Manyberries

"Now you've got it," Harry Charles congratulated Four-Eyed Tom. "The thing is, nobody's going to get out of the car to see a retired politician, but they'll drive a thousand miles to see something dumb or stupid. They'd be flocking here from all over."

"Yeah, but they'd be thinking Manyberries is dumb or stupid and who wants to live in a town that people think is dumb or stupid?" None of this was making sense to Purvis, or to the rest of us for that matter.

"Who cares what they think? If people are coming here from all over to see what they think is the eighth wonder of the world of dumb, and spending their money while they're here, what do we care?" Harry Charles was rubbing his thumb and forefinger together in the universal sign for cash. "Do you think they're gonna roll right down the main street and not stop off here at the Ranchmen's where they can see the people who elected Ralph as Mayor and appointed him to Chair of the Olympics Committee? Don't you think it even a little bit possible they might offer to buy some of the yokels a drink just to say they met one or two of the dumbest people in the dumbest town on the planet?"

"You're on to something here," Perley said. "If somebody offered to buy me a drink or two, who cares what they think when they leave, or even what they thought before they arrived?"

"And, in terms of the survival of the Ranchmen's, every time somebody buys us a drink, we mark that down as a drink we can buy ourselves in the future with the money we saved. Right there you've got the underpinnings of the mission statement of the Ranchmen's Preservation Committee. Every free drink for one of us means a future sale for the Ranchmen's."

"You know, this could work," Perley said. "You had me in doubt there, thinking it was a hare-brained scheme that was going to go nowhere."

"Harry Charles," I interrupted, "would you consider moving to Ottawa and accepting the Presidency of the National Press Club of Canada?"

"No, I couldn't live in a steam bath in summer and iceberg in winter. But on this other thing you just have to remember," Harry Charles told us, "there are no dumber people on earth than those who think they're smarter, cleverer or more sophisticated than everybody else. And, it has been my experience that they're the ones who'll spend the most money trying to prove it."

The Manyberries Cathouse

I've had a lot of relationships with cats, not all of them bad. In fact, with each and every cat I've ever known I think I can honestly say there was probably a minute or two where the relationship was almost good.

Harry Charles, who said cats were do-nothing deadbeats living off the generosity of people who didn't have sense enough to get a good hunting dog, attracted cats like a magnet attracts metal shavings.

He would go into a house and if a cat lived there it would make a beeline for him and jump up into his lap purring and then settle down.

I don't remember the first cat in our family when I was a child but my mother told me her name was Minnie and she was golden coloured, sort of like a palomino horse, I guess.

The first cat we owned after we married stayed briefly with us and when our daughter was born, moved in with my mother-in-law. His name was Fagan, a name given to him by friends who often went outside to smoke strangely scented cigarettes and stare off into other worlds.

Fagan was pure white and had reddish eyes. He had to leave because he was too curious about the infant in the crib and we feared he might think she was a soft cushion on which to sleep. His departure was made easier by the fact that the apartment in which we lived had an absolutely no pets policy. They also had an absolutely no children policy so we left not long after Fagan did. I told Fagan when I dropped him off that he was fortunate he wasn't being "moved to the farm". Moving to the farm for cats and dogs is not a good move.

The next cat was Mitt, who had four white socks and grew up into a very large cat. Mitt could have played a blocker on a professional cat football team or could have been a cat sumo wrestler. Mitt was a pretty good cat because he more or less adopted Charlie, our first dog. If the big dog down the road came along and growled at Charlie through our gate, he'd often get a bloody nose from the claws on Mitt's front right paw. I say often because it takes some dogs years to realize that if you stick your nose in between pickets and growl and a cat gives you a good raking, chances are it might happen again. And it did happen again, many times, until that German shepherd saw the light bulb over his head.

Mitt got very old and finally "went to the farm". Kids love to imagine their cats gambolling in the hayloft of a barn, or playing with a string and paper in the farmyard.

We didn't have any cats for a while and that was okay with me. But then the neighbour's cat had kittens when Jennifer was seven, and we were back in the cat business. Her name was Indy, short for Indianapolis because of the way she raced to find a hiding place whenever somebody knocked or rang the bell at the front door.

Then when son Michael was about six that same neighbour's cat had another litter and he brought home a half-sibling as a companion. He called his cat Knob, as in dumb as a doorknob. But it turned out Knob was Miss Knob and she had a litter. Getting rid of cats is not as easy as getting them. It took a while before every one of those kittens had found a home. I can assure you that not one of them "went to live on a farm".

But she was as dumb as a doorknob because on Mike's 10th birthday she ran in front of a car. One of the kids at his party was just leaving and returned to tell us Knob was on the street in front of the house and badly injured. I took her to the vet and learned why vets retire in splendid comfort. The vet called me at home to say she was beyond saving. Emergency care and the little needle that sent her "to the farm" set me back $500.

I think his next cat was named Boston and he stayed a while with us and one day went out and never returned. We weren't worried that he might have inadvertently "gone to the farm". Boston hardly ever ate at our house and yet always appeared well fed. We think he found a place that served better food than cat chow and decided to move in there.

Not to be deterred, Michael visited the neighbour not long after and found that their most prolific cat had produced yet another litter. Thus the all black Spook came to live with us. He should have been called Knob too because he would try to rub against your shins when you were sitting and inevitably bang his head on the chair leg.

Spook developed appetite problems and began losing weight. I trundled him to the vet, who told me he had to have several teeth removed due to a gum disease. That set me back close to $500. Harry Charles said he could have done it with needle nose pliers and would have charged no more than a pint or two of beer.

Jennifer now had Indy and Michael had Spook and we all had Charlie and Hank the Weimaraner had all of us.

Skip ahead many years and now Jennifer and Michael are moving into their own homes. Well, you just can't leave home with your cats, can you? Nope, we had Indy and Spook for eternity.

Then Jennifer came in one day and said a friend's cat had a new litter of kittens and they were talking about sending them "to the farm". I said too bad and went on reading the newspaper. Then she mentioned one of the kittens was golden coloured, sort of like a palomino.

I don't know how it happened but all of a sudden we were going to get a new cat. Indy was sort of calico, Spook was jet black and this new cat would be golden. Designer/decorator cats, I guess.

I argued that if a new animal was going to join the existing menagerie, I was going to name him and, I warned sternly, it had better be a him.

When Jennifer brought him home, I said his name was TLC and Jennifer said, "ahhh, Dad, that's sweet, Tender Love and Care."

I said, "The hell that's what it means. TLC means The Last Cat."

The strange thing about TLC was he never meowed. He would try to play with Indy and Spook and he'd get batted severely about the head and ears and chased and bitten for good measure. Old cats don't appreciate new cats invading their territory and routine. They don't like it so much they do everything possible to keep the new one from even eating. TLC developed a severe inferiority complex and stayed downstairs by himself. He'd only come upstairs when the other two were sound asleep. But they'd wake up when they'd hear him crunching the cat chow and rouse themselves to chase him back downstairs.

Finally, it came to pass that both Indy and Spook were severely old. They were so old that something had to be done and that something was going to be a "trip to the farm".

Michael sought out a holistic veterinarian and all four of us went with them on their final journey. Only Michael and I went into the surgery room. He put them on the high table facing each other and the vet came in and gave them a gentle tranquilizer. When they were relaxed, he gave them each an injection and they went to sleep looking at each other, much as they had gone to sleep over the previous 16 years.

The damn wind was kicking up dust outside that vet's office and it made my eyes water because of my allergies but Michael held up pretty well.

So now only TLC is left and he is one changed cat. He can meow, has the run of the house, is bold enough to jump up on the bed and insists on being petted at night and first thing in the morning.

It's a good thing his name is TLC because I think he'd hate it if another cat came and invaded his territory and routine.

It isn't going to happen. It can't happen because we'd have to change his name and he's too old now to learn any new tricks.

The Manyberries Rainmaker

It can get awful hot and dry in Manyberries in the spring and summer. We don't always get rain when farmers need it and sometimes when it does rain, it evaporates faster than an election campaign promise.

We won't concede that Manyberries is in a dry belt just because somebody once said we were and the uproar continues today. As one of the old timers tells it, that was back in the early 1900s and people here have long memories even if they weren't there to witness it.

But even though we won't admit to being a less-than-sufficient moisture area, there was a time when Manyberries got on the rainmaker bandwagon. Or sucker list, as Harry Charles prefers to call it.

Seems there was an intolerably long dry spell back around 1919 and folks were getting desperate for rain, especially in spring when they needed moisture for germination of the crops they planted.

"There was this fellow who came up from California after getting a letter from some of the town big shots in Medicine Hat," Harry Charles told us one night. "They had read of his amazing ability to produce rain clouds and offered him a sack full of cash if he could make it rain in the district around their town."

Harry Charles went on to say they struck a hard bargain whereby this California gentleman, by the name of Charles Hatfield, would produce rain and be paid generously for his miracle. He was to work in the May/June/July quarter when the crops really need their refreshment.

They agreed that he would not be paid for the first two inches of rain he produced but that he would get $4,000 for the next two and another $4,000 for two more inches after that. "That was a pretty fair chunk of change back then," Harry Charles said, "but worth every penny if he made it rain on time for spring planting and summer moisture."

"So, he was going to be paid as much as $8,000 for producing six inches of rain?" It sounded to me like Mr. Hatfield was either crazy or on to something miraculous.

"Yep, $8,000 for six inches of rain and both sides considered that an honest deal. But here's the hitch: the contract covered those three months and what the big shots in town didn't know or maybe wanted to forget was the average rainfall for that area in those three months is just over six inches. This Hatfield guy was betting on a four-legged horse running against a three-legged milk cow."

Harry Charles went on to describe what he had read about Mr. Hatfield's rain-making contraption and I could see Purvis getting antsy and excited.

Hatfield's contraption was a tower, not high enough to reach the clouds but high enough to impress the folks who went out to see it. It was taller than the Methodist church steeple that was reduced in height some years later by lightning.

There isn't a kid around who doesn't like towers and things you can climb so high you can almost touch the clouds and Purvis is no exception.

What Hatfield did, so would Purvis. He'd build a tower higher than Hatfield could have imagined and he'd put sauce pans and pots up on top just like Hatfield did on his tower back in 1919.

Purvis had a head start on his project because he had purchased an old windmill tower some years back after they invented electricity. Windmills became obsolete because electricity begat electric water pumps. Who wants to climb a tower to do maintenance when all you have to do is flick a switch when the cows get thirsty or the turnips need watering? Purvis bought it, took it apart piece by piece, hauled it home and spent part of the next summer erecting it in his backyard. He has been setting aside a little money every year since in the hope he can hire a drilling rig that will find water in abundance beneath his backyard. His plan was to raise money to build a waterworks system and incorporate as the Purvis Manyberries Waterworks Corporation. He figured if all 37 homes in Manyberries signed on as customers, and the wind kept blowing, he'd have a healthy pension supplement for life. But, alas, it wasn't to be.

Mrs. Purvis forced him to dismantle the tower because she didn't want it in the backyard serving as a landmark for anyone who would use it to find their way to Manyberries for nefarious reasons. Mrs. Purvis stopped looking up at the sky the day the Russians launched Sputnik because she was sure it meant the world would end. When it comes to potential alien danger, Mrs. Purvis believes you can't be too cautious.

So the Purvis backyard was ruled out as a location for the rainmaker tower, but Harry Charles had a suggestion: why not ask Old Rutherford if Purvis could use the second unused acre on his lot for the tower. "Old Rutherford and the Mrs like to sunbathe nude up to the northeast where the sand dune is. I bet if you allowed them to climb the tower to sunbathe nude up on the platform closer to the sun, he'd be pleased to let you erect the tower there."

The real motive behind Harry Charles' suggestion was that the Rutherfords had discovered a sandy area right in the middle of one of our favourite antelope hunting spots and he was worried that the sight of them out there naked on the prairie would drive the antelope all the way to Saskatchewan or down into Montana. Antelope have excellent eyesight and are pretty sensitive creatures. "Geez, if they got a glimpse of Old Rutherford and the Mrs naked, they could scoot south all the way down to Montana. We might have to eat beef this winter if this keeps up."

Purvis had a visit with Old Rutherford and found an enthusiastic response. The old guy wasn't sure if his wife could climb the tower but he knew he could, so Purvis was welcome to his second acre. The first acre is where the house sits and where Old Rutherford grows his turnips and carrots and other vegetables they put down in the root cellar. He figured if the tower produced rain, he'd get a secondary bonus in that he wouldn't have to pump and haul water for his garden.

So construction began on the tower. Purvis had saved most of the nuts and bolts in pails, and most of the struts and braces were still intact except for a couple that his nephew tried to turn into unbreakable hockey sticks.

By day five the tower was progressing nicely when we found we were short on plywood for the platform. This caused a delay in construction while we waited for somebody to plan a trip to Medicine Hat to bring back a thick sheet of plywood along with the groceries.

By day 12 the tower was just about finished with the platform installed and bolted securely and safely about six feet from the top, where Purvis planned to install a rooster weather vane he had salvaged from a barn that had blown down years before.

The only problem was that nobody knew what secret chemicals Mr. Hatfield from California had put in the pans and pails he placed on his platform back in 1919 to make it rain.

"I wouldn't have anything with alcohol in your chemicals,

Purvis," Harry Charles said. "There's a chance Old Rutherford could get up there and find it to his liking and you wouldn't want him wandering around on that platform or coming down the ladder on anything less than steady legs."

So Purvis put salt and vinegar in one pail and Tabasco sauce and water in another and for the third he mixed salt and water and we retired to the Ranchmen's to toast his work and wish him luck.

We'd hardly taken our chairs when Perley walked in with his mailbag still bulging. "Old Rutherford is up on your tower platform, Purvis," he announced. "He's already gathering sunshine and the Mrs is halfway up and looks like she's gonna make it."

"Geez, if my wife ever looks up and sees that, she'll think the aliens are invading for sure," Purvis said.

"Well, at least if they're up there, they won't be over by the sand dunes where we hunt antelope," Perley said as he gulped down a short glass of beer and wiped his lips. "I have to finish my rounds but I'll keep an eye on the two of them and let you know if they have any problems."

"Just hope that if this thing works, it doesn't bring lightning with it," Purvis said. "It'd be terrible if Old Rutherford and the Mrs got whacked by a lightning bolt. My wife would take that as another sign the space invaders are getting closer."

As it turned out, there was no lightning and no rain. Old Rutherford got a lot of work done on his suntan, though, and all anyone had to do was look up at that weathervane rooster to see which way the wind was blowing. Of course they didn't really have to look up because the wind always comes from the west and if it isn't coming from the west, it'll be from north or east and there's nothing you can do about it anyway.

But sometimes the wind can blow pretty hard on Manyberries and some months later we had a big windstorm while I was out of town one day.

When I drove back and parked at the Ranchmen's I looked over to the tower to see which way the west wind was blowing and the tower was gone.

At our table inside, Harry Charles, Perley and Purvis were nursing their beer and talking quietly.

"What happened to the tower? Old Rutherford get tired of it?" I asked.

"Nope, it blew down," Purvis said. "That big wind got it rocking and next thing you know she was swaying more and more and finally she swayed too far over and then just crashed to the ground."

Anybody get hurt?"

"Nope, Old Rutherford could have been, but he's pretty fast on his feet and with his brain, for a guy that old," Perley told me. Old Rutherford is probably no more than two or three years older than Perley but his sun tanning has made him a little more leathery.

"What happened was Old Rutherford was up on the platform sun tanning when the wind came up and it happened too quick for him to make his way back down the ladder," Harry Charles took up the story. They all defer to Harry Charles because he is a lot more succinct in his story telling.

"Old Rutherford got on the high side of the thing because he knew which way she would fall and he rode her down. But right at the end, just before it hit the ground, he pushed off with his bare feet and jumped up and away so it was like he was going against gravity. He came down soft as a feather as if he had only jumped a few inches off the ground, and never broke a sweat or a bone."

"Geez, I read somewhere that you could save yourself that way if you were in an elevator and the cables broke, so it does work." I was excited to know that a childhood nightmare had a workable solution.

"Yes, but in an elevator you can't see the bottom so you'll never know when to jump and it'll hit bottom while you're standing there with your knees bent ready to jump." Harry Charles had an answer for everything. "Next thing you know, your hips will be up between your shoulders."

"Still, a pretty smart move for Old Rutherford," I said.

"Yeah, it was," Purvis said, "and I'm relieved he wasn't hurt and that his Mrs wasn't under it when it crashed. But I've got a bigger problem now" he said. "My wife happened to look out the window at the very moment the tower was coming down and you can imagine what she thought when she saw Old Rutherford, stark naked, flying through the air on that thing and making that miracle jump just before it landed. Now she's walking around the house with her eyes glued to the floor and I don't believe she'll ever look up again." Purvis paused.

"Not that I would myself if I had to see Old Rutherford and all his parts flying through the air like that."

Hank the Hustler

Naming a dog is a lot more complicated than naming a child, especially if the dog is a purebred. Hank's full handle was Smokey City's Calgary Hank. Smokey City was the name of the kennel where he was born in Pennsylvania. We were advised to work that in on the possibility Hank might some day become an important dog and somebody might want him to become a father. Smokey City had such a great reputation, it was important to let people know that Hank was a descendant of some of the best of his breed. I stuck Hank in there because it always sounded to me like a hunter's name.

Hank was as good a hunting dog as any hunter ever could have partnered with. Harry Charles and Perley said we were the best-matched dog and hunter team they ever saw. Both of us were, one of us still is, bone lazy hunters. Hank and I never saw a hill that was worth climbing and would walk for miles to get around one rather than hundreds of yards to get over it. And while the other guys and their dogs would be out racing around looking for birds, Hank and I were usually content to find a soft spot to sit and watch them. If they put up a bird and it flew our way, I didn't mind rousing myself to shoot it and Hank didn't mind rousing himself to go over and fetch it. And if I missed, as is often the case, we were never terribly disappointed, if the sun was warm and there was just a light breeze.

Not that Hank wouldn't hunt hard if the situation required him to. It's just that he adopted whatever pace I set and wasn't the complaining type if that pace wouldn't wind a tortoise.

But one time he did go way beyond the call of duty and that's when I shot a goose on a very windy day.

We were hunting near a large slough when a Chinook wind was blowing hard out of the west. We weren't looking for migratory birds because it was a little too early in the season and the big flocks hadn't yet come down from the north. Our plan was to put up some partridge; we were hoping this wouldn't take long because I had brought along a really good minced beef sandwich lunch with a thermos of tea and one well chilled bottle of beer.

We were rounding the south end of the slough when the geese came over. They were what we call speckle bellies and were flying in a straight-line formation. I fired at the leading bird and the one in the rear buckled and splashed down in the slough.

You have to know that out on the prairie when the Chinook wind is blowing hard, the waves can get high and very choppy.

Hank saw the bird splash down and went for it, ignoring my call to come back. I figured the wind would float it to shore and neither of us would have to do any work. For some reason known only to him, Hank wanted to expend some energy by fetching it.

The bird had fallen at least a hundred yards from shore and when he got 25 yards out, all I could see of Hank now and then was his head bobbing up and over the waves. The rest of the time he was in the troughs.

When he reached the spot where he thought the bird had fallen, he started swimming in circles. And he swam and he swam some more. And he kept swimming until I thought he was in danger of wearing himself out. I blew the dog whistle hard and he still kept swimming. I blew harder and finally got his attention. He turned and started swimming back to me and it took him a lot longer to get back than it did to get out there. When he reached shore, he did something uncharacteristic for Hank. He flopped right down in the mud and stayed there until his breathing was back to near normal.

I gave him a few good rubs on the ears and went over to the grass to sit down. After a while, Hank came over and stretched out beside me on the grass and I told him he was going to have to go back in the water to get all the mud off his belly.

It's funny, when you're out on the prairie in a howling Chinook wind, how comfortable you can get by stretching out in the grass. With the sun shining down and the grass giving you a little shelter against the wind, you can fall sound asleep, and that's what we did.

When I woke up, I decided I'd walk the shore where I thought the waves would deposit my goose, and we'd pick it up and go for lunch. I looked over and Hank wasn't there. I gave him a short whistle and he didn't come so I sat up and looked around.

He was back in the water, way out in the middle of the slough, looking for that goose. I had to give him several whistle blasts before he turned and headed back to shore and he repeated his earlier action of flopping down in the mud while he caught his breath.

And God Created Manyberries

While he was resting I walked the shoreline looking for the goose. I decided if I spotted it, I would go back and get Hank and give him the honour of finding and fetching it. He deserved at least that after all his swimming work.

Well, there was no goose anywhere so I whistled Hank to come and then headed to a field to the west to look for partridge.

We got a few and headed back to the slough and the Suburban parked beyond that. Hank ran ahead and plunged back into the water. He was not going to let that goose go to waste.

This time he swam in even larger circles and one of the circles was so big he wound up on the opposite side of the slough. He flopped down in the mud and I started walking around to meet him.

We never did find that goose. We circled that slough completely and never saw any bird, dead or alive. Hank took one more swim and I sat and worried a little, thinking if it had been me, I'd have sunk to the bottom by now.

Is there a point to this? Well, sort of.

Two weeks later we were back at that slough and this time it was to get a few ducks. We had barely reached the shore when Hank went plunging into the water and made a beeline for just about exactly where that goose had fallen two weeks earlier.

He did the whole swimming in circles again and must have made about six big circles before I whistled him back. Again, he flopped in the mud while he caught his breath.

When I told Harry Charles about this he got a little misty-eyed.

"That's as good a dog as any man could ever be owned by," he said. He reached over and gave Hank an ear rub.

"I don't know if there's any moral to your story," Harry Charles said, "but if there is, it's gotta be that humans could learn a helluva lot if they paid more attention to their dogs."

"About what?" I asked.

"Oh, I don't know, maybe about how if you've got a job to do, that you do it. Or maybe about never giving up. Or maybe about doing what you can to help your friend no matter how long it takes or how hard the work is when you're doing the helping."

I was reminded of this not long ago when Old Rutherford called me at 4:30 one morning and asked if I could bring my jumper cables over and help him get his ancient Pontiac station wagon started. It was close to 30 below and there was a helluva wind from the north and that bed was so warm, but I went anyway.

After I got the Pontiac running and Old Rutherford and the Mrs on their way to a medical appointment in Medicine Hat, I drove home and found myself hoping that Hank would be proud of me.

A Manyberries Hero

A bunch of us were sitting around the table at the Ranchmen's discussing the upcoming November 11th Remembrance Day and somehow the topic shifted to the heroes of Manyberries and the lack thereof.

Perley, the only local link we have with the federal government, got excited at the prospect of us applying for a federal grant to identify and honour our local heroes.

Harry Charles said that the chance of Manyberries getting a grant for anything was skinnier than half of one of old Rutherford's legs. Old Rutherford is often seen wearing short pants of the sort you see pictures of some golfers wearing. There are some men, and women, who should not wear short pants and he is definitely part of that crowd.

It reminds me of the time when I was wearing cut-off blue jeans while teaching my eight-year-old son and one of his buddies how to use a wedge to hit golf balls. The young buddy turned to Mike as I walked down the slope of the school yard to fetch a couple of balls and said, "Gee, Mike, are your Dad's legs ever skinny."

Mike told me later, "You know, Dad, you don't have to wear cut-off jeans if you don't want to."

I haven't worn anything but long pants since then and will never wear cut-offs or even those fancy Bermuda shorts for as long as I live.

So I am in the same category as Old Rutherford but he is oblivious to the fact that dogs look at him in his shorts and drool as they think of bones for gnawing.

With these images of Old Rutherford pretty well ending any hopes we might have entertained for receiving a generous federal

And God Created Manyberries

cultural grant, we changed the subject to a discussion about how Manyberries could have its own pantheon of heroes.

We have all the traditional heroes of any town in the British Commonwealth because almost all of us sent our brave and noble off to fight in various wars. Lads from the area have seen engagement in the Boer War, World Wars One and Two, and Korea. Some of those lads didn't come back but we recognize that they, and the ones who did return, are heroes. As Governor General Adrienne Clarkson once said in a eulogy for the Unknown Soldier, "He has become part of us forever. And we are part of him."

But we were thinking along the lines of heroes such as Gene Autry or Roy Rogers, or even Clint Eastwood in some of his cowboy movies. Somebody mentioned Brad Pitt but Harry Charles had seen the video of Brad where he fights a grizzly bear and said "that is not heroic, that is crazy."

Then somebody recalled there was a photo around somewhere of a posse of Manyberries area ranchers and cowboys, all armed to the teeth and mounted. The caption with that photo said they had organized the posse almost a hundred years ago to go after some bank robbers.

Perley said if we could find that photograph and get it blown up into life size and framed, maybe we could hang it on the wall of the Ranchmen's and it could become a tourist attraction. "These are wild west heroes like you see in the movies," he said. "People'd come from all over to see the photograph and we could put a caption below it telling them these are the wild west heroes of Manyberries."

Harry Charles remembered seeing the photograph years earlier. "As I recall," he said, "those men were riding what appeared to be draught horses with some of them still in harness. Some were wearing overalls and hats with earflaps. I don't recall seeing one high-heeled boot on any of them. And finally," he said, "they weren't carrying any guns."

Well, that description kind of quieted everybody down. If you put a picture like that up on the wall of the Ranchmen's the first thing somebody would say is you got a picture of a bunch of farmers and we all knew that.

Perley rose to the challenge. "We'll change the caption," he said. "We'll call them the farmer heroes of Manyberries. These are the men who, with their wives, settled this country and started the agriculture industry that brought food to the hungry of the world."

"A noble sentiment," Harry Charles said, "but I don't think it's going to draw too many people up from Hollywood."

When I left they were making up lists of who got the most home runs back in the days when Manyberries had a baseball team.

The Manyberries Pie Bake-Off

It was Purvis who got it started when he bragged about his pies and how the "boys at the hunt camp swear up and down my pies are the best they've ever eaten."

In reality there is no hunt camp, at least not the sort of permanent hunt camp easterners recognize. Purvis and his sons and grandsons and some nephews head out every November and haul trailers to wherever they're going to stay. The location varies from year to year but it is never more than a half-hour drive from a place where they can re-stock their refreshments and groceries. Purvis takes charge of all the arrangements including making a menu for every meal and buying all the supplies. Everybody chips in an equal amount, except those who haven't yet reached legal drinking age; they get a pass on the expenses because that's where most of the money is spent.

One of the highlights of the year's menu is the 10 pound pot of chilli con carne Mrs. Purvis prepares and freezes solid. It is placed most reverently in a cooler with beer and various cocktail mixes where it stays frozen and keeps the beverages cool. It is not ever eaten until the final evening before the return home. Purvis likes his chilli spicy smouldering hot and Mrs. Purvis obliges him with crushed scotch bonnet peppers and very generous splashes of Tabasco sauce. We've all accompanied the Purvis gang on hunts over the years and agree that Mrs. Purvis' chilli is lava hot. Perley says you know you've had authentic Purvis chilli when your haemorrhoids hum the next morning. He says the Purvis chilli hum could drown out the sound of three cathedral choirs in pre-concert warm-up.

The other menu highlight is the pie Purvis brings along and doesn't include in the expense tally. That and the chilli are his reward to the others for letting him be the chief organizer. There are pies for dessert for every meal except breakfast and always enough that everybody gets a generous slice. Depending on the number of hunters in any given year there could be as many as three pies at every meal.

The year I joined them one of the meals was a two-pie event: meat pie for the main course followed by apple pie for dessert. That was also the year Purvis read something by Ernest Hemingway and decided civilized hunters should have pre-dinner gin martinis which meant in turn somebody had to drive the half hour into Medicine Hat to get gin and vermouth and plastic martini glasses.

Purvis believes in variety too, because he'll have peach, apple, blueberry (canned), chocolate, cherry, sweet potato, pumpkin and buttered raisin, so that you never have to eat the same pie twice on the same day. He brings them from frozen state to lovingly warmed in a special camp stove oven one of his sons fashioned out of scrap tin from a chicken shed roof. I bought a gallon of vanilla ice cream in addition to the gin, vermouth and plastic glasses when we made the run into Medicine Hat. Purvis wasn't at all insulted and said he wished he had thought of it. That was the night of the two-pie dinner.

Well, when Purvis got to bragging about his pies in the Ranchmen's that night, Perley said he agreed that Purvis' pies were fine but not as good as the pies he cooked from time to time.

It was December and the hunting season had ended and Perley was very well refreshed after making many stops at many homes to deliver mail and enjoying pre-Christmas libations with the people on his route (these plus surplus from backyard gardens being the only remuneration Perley gets for looking after the mail in Manyberries).

It was Harry Charles who egged them on until it was decided we'd have a best pie bake-off that would be open to any man in Manyberries who wanted to bake a pie. The judges would be the wives of the participants and they would have to swear that they had no hand in the preparations.

The entry fee would be five dollars and there would be only one winner with no second or third place ribbons. All contestants would have to pledge to underwrite the cost of all drinks consumed that night at the Ranchmen's with his winnings. The deal was done and it was left to Purvis, Perley and Harry Charles to sort out the details.

I decided, in a moment of bravado, to enter the bake-off and informed the trio. They all snorted and Harry Charles remarked that I probably couldn't bake a cow flap on the prairie in a whole hot summer.

When you decide to have a momentous event like this in

Manyberries, you don't do it in a hurry. You want to have two or three months after the initial decision so people will have time to plan and to talk and to make side wagers. It gives the participants time to dream about winning and all the glory that would accrue. They have to have time to savour the prospect of winning and the months of bragging rights they'll earn. The bake-off would be held on the last day of February, which would help pass the first two months of the year and alleviate the post-Christmas letdown.

Through Christmas and New Year celebrations and the drear of January, all that anybody talked about was the pie bake-off. One contestant would announce he was thinking about apple cinnamon and then a week later change his mind and say he was favouring a peach pie with secret ingredients. Somebody else would say he was thinking about calling a cousin in Kelowna and asking for a shipment of cherries that she had picked from her own tree and frozen. One guy wondered about substituting plantains for bananas and Four-Eyed Tom said he'd never heard of plantation pie.

Purvis and Perley kept their cards right up against their vests and never once mentioned what they had in mind to bake. Harry Charles had lobbied hard to be a judge and not a contestant because his favourite food is pie and besides, he said, "you've gotta have at least one male on the judging panel to give it balance."

In total we had 51 pies in the Ranchmen's on bake-off night. Seventeen contestants had brought three each so there'd be enough for the judges to taste and some left for the curious who showed up for the event.

The contestants were all nervous, some even a little giggly, and it wasn't just what we were drinking that made us that way. This was a big event, the biggest of the year to date, and the winner would have bragging rights at least until planting time and the opening of fishing season.

I tasted slivers of pie from each contestant and there wasn't one that I would not have gone back to for seconds. But only one pie could win and the winner was a sweet potato pie that had my name on it. The judges said they loved the hint of clove and cinnamon and the slivered almonds on top with the fresh thick and sweetened cream poured over each slice.

I had to stand and swear in public that my wife did not help me in any way but did admit that the cream was purchased. That did not disqualify me because none of the other contestants had a cow or means of making fresh- from-the-cow cream. But my confession further endeared me to the lady judges and even Harry Charles seemed impressed by my honesty.

Later that night when the crowd had dispersed, Perley was chuckling about Purvis losing.

"I don't think there were any losers," I said, "I think every entrant was a winner."

"Geez", Perley said, "you sound like a Canadian. The fact is you beat Purvis and he was the guy who said he made the best pies in the world."

"Besides," Harry Charles added, "do you really think Purvis could have stood up there in front of that crowd and sworn he had no help whatsoever from his wife? I doubt it because those pies he takes hunting always come pre-baked and frozen. And, remember, he says they're his pies but never once over the years has he ever claimed he baked them. He just calls them his pies. And all he swore was that he never left the kitchen during the whole baking process."

Nobody was going to outright accuse Purvis of pie cheating but Harry Charles' remarks left a question mark hanging over Purvis' pie integrity.

When we were leaving, Harry Charles said to Perley that they were due soon for a visit with old Joe Tschetter at the Hutterite colony to talk about hunting birds there come the autumn.

"You should come along with us," Perley said, turning to me.

"Well, maybe if I have time," I said. "Things could get busy in the coming weeks and well, if I can find time and it's the right day, I might be able to slip away."

"Oh, you've gotta come along," Harry Charles said. "We can go before noon and hope that old Joe invites us to stay for lunch. If we're lucky, maybe Mrs. Tschetter will have one of her beautiful sweet potato pies in the oven."

"Did old Joe tell you or did she?" I asked.

"Nobody told us and we won't tell anybody either," Perley assured me. "You told the truth when you said your wife didn't help you in any way and best of all, you beat Purvis." And he slapped me on the back.

"But adding that fresh-from-the-cow thick sweetened cream and the slivered almonds was what did it for me as a judge," Harry Charles slapped me on the back too. Mrs. Tschetter just serves her pies plain."

"But, what you didn't earn was endless bragging rights about your victory through until spring," Perley cautioned. "We'll give you the next five nights to brag about it at the Ranchmen's and then you've gotta stop. Unless, of course Purvis is there and then you can brag about it all you want."

The Manyberries
Political Analyst

Old Rutherford walked into the Ranchmen's with a newspaper tucked under his arm the way you see models posing as businessmen in pictures in big, slick magazines. On his way to his preferred table he dropped the newspaper in front of us and suggested we should read it if we were interested in what's going on in the world. It was a fairly recent edition of a Toronto newspaper.

"Toronto isn't the world," Harry Charles said to Old Rutherford's back as Perley grabbed the paper and began flipping through to find the horoscope page. "In fact, it isn't even the centre of the universe, or even Ontario for that matter."

"Must be some big shot Toronto tycoon in town," Purvis observed. "Probably choppered in to look at one of those new well-sites over to the east. For the life of me I can't understand how watching a crew set up for a new derrick makes anyone any wiser as an investment advisor."

We don't get too many big city newspapers in Manyberries unless some high mucky-muck business type passes through and drops a copy in the café or one in the men's room. When we do find one, it gets passed from hand to hand so everyone can catch up on what the crazy people are doing.

When Perley had finished reading his horoscope, Harry Charles took the front section and gave it a scan. "Story in here says Stephen Harper might rearrange his Cabinet," he told us, "and it says Peter MacKay might be shifted to another post because he allegedly referred to Belinda as a dog. Cripes almighty, that was months ago and they're still dragging that back into their stories." He sighed

And God Created Manyberries

before continuing. "Well, I guess that passes for political analysis in the media these days."

It's not widely known, except by the chosen and cognizant, that Harry Charles is Manyberries' political analyst in residence. He writes a column twice a year for a small, quality publication called The Bald Prairie Tattler, which is published by the Bald Prairie Rattlers' Hunting and Fishing Club.

In a busy year, the Club boasts a membership of 28, five of whom were sitting at the table. That would be Harry Charles, Purvis, Perley, Four-Eyed Tom and me.

The rest of the membership is scattered across the region and they're mostly farmers, ranchers, a few rig pigs who read and a couple of guys from Calgary who come down every year to hunt pheasants.

They print the Tattler on an old mimeograph machine that was on its way to the dump after a school some miles from here was able to purchase a photocopier. One of these days they hope to get the photocopier when the school is able to purchase computers and high speed printers.

Anyway, the Bald Prairie Tattler is mostly filled with news that will interest the members: items about hunting, fishing, gun control, who got the biggest buck or pheasant and whose hunting dog died. It's pretty critical information for the membership and copies are left at the Ranchmen's for pickup. The guys who come down from Calgary get their copies 10 months later than the rest of us but understand that the club has no membership fees and thus no money for mailing.

Harry Charles fills the back page with his political analysis and isn't afraid to tackle even the most contentious issues, like gun control and political cynicism. He is philosophically conservative but is a man of such journalistic integrity he never lets that influence or slant his carefully considered writing.

For instance, in one column a few years ago, he wrote about the plan of two national political parties with the support of one from Quebec (not the Official Opposition Conservatives) to take every hunting rifle and shotgun in Canada and bend the barrels at 90 degree angles. And, he warned his readers, that was only the first step. In the following years, they were going to bend those barrels so they were u-shaped. It was a plan, he wrote, to eliminate hunters. On the first bend, the bullets would be hitting any hunters to the right or left of the shooter, depending on which way the barrel was bent. The final u-bend would eliminate the gun owner. People who rely on big city newspapers never read even a hint of that while the debate raged in Parliament.

In another, when ducks were dying by the score on Pakowki Lake from an avian botulism outbreak, he very carefully took his readers to the heart of the matter so they could decide on their own the reason and who was to blame. "What," he asked in his column, "is behind this kill-off of our ducks? Could it be that the Liberals and New Democrats refused to support a massive botulism inoculation of the entire migratory bird population because of their hostility towards the Americans? They know that the ducks go south to winter in the United States. Is it an attempt to sabotage our American hunting compatriots?"

Harry Charles says modestly that unlike his counterparts in Ottawa he has 12 months to contemplate and probe for the insights he delivers and that is why his readers accept every word as gospel and embrace the political analysis he proffers without challenge. It's the kind of political insight you just can't get from the daily or weekly newspapers.

Some years back winter came early and hard and the ducks and geese gave us a fly-past on their way to warmer American climes. It wasn't the early cold weather that was to blame at all, Harry Charles informed his readers. It was the supporters of a certain two parties (not the Official Opposition Conservatives) who came out here from the big city by bus and shooed the ducks and geese out of the sloughs and fields so the hunters would be left holding empty game bags.

There's no way of knowing how many people read the four pages (printed both sides) of the 28 copies of the Bald Prairie Tattler that are published twice a year, but we think it's a massive number and that it has influence far greater than any other publication available. People out here look for depth in what they read and not for what fancy shoes or new hairstyles adorn the politicians or whether they resemble or act like dogs.

"Well, I believe Canadians want a balanced perspective from those who offer analysis or commentary on national affairs," Harry Charles said. "And I'm certainly not going to put my name over anything that would leave me open to accusations of political bias."

And God Created Manyberries

When Dogs Don't Fly

"I guess you and Hank won't be flying anywhere to hunt next fall," Perley said, "because they won't let him on the airplane."

"I don't think either one of us, and I think I can speak for him, was saving our loonies for any trips much beyond Etzikom. Unless of course there are three or four other guys who want to split the cost of gasoline."

Etzikom is a bit west of Manyberries and there are rumoured to be pheasants in the area. Hank and I drove every road for miles around in my Suburban and never saw one. We were almost at the point of getting out of the vehicle and walking around a bit to see if we couldn't actually raise a bird.

"I don't know why Air Canada wouldn't accept Hank but would let you aboard, dressed the way you do to go hunting."

I am not what you might call a classy dresser when I go hunting. I wear an old red Coors golf cap that I got at a golf tournament back in the century when I worked in radio. I wear a blaze orange shotgunner's vest that I picked up at a flea market for 50 cents and it's hardly torn at all. The dog whistle attached to it by a cord came with it. I never use the whistle because Hank generally likes to walk with me when we hunt and not out in front like certain overly ambitious dogs do for their humans. I have one pair of blue jeans that are worn so thin they're more like silk that only comes out of the hunting bag for the season. I've been following this routine with the jeans for nearly 20 years. My other two pairs of jeans are for dress up and everyday wear. There's a red shirt I wear under the vest with most of the lower buttons missing as a result of outward pressure. It's about the same age as the jeans except the shirt wasn't customized with a strong elastic band in the back to compensate for that outward pressure. I bought the boots that complete the ensemble at Sears 30 years ago on sale and they're holding up better than the body above them.

"The thing is, Hank always looks classy when he wears his blaze orange collar and you look more like his bearer than his human." A bearer is, I think, the guy who walks behind a rich hunter carrying the extra shotgun.

"It's always a pleasant break from the routine of strenuously avoiding doing anything to come in here and have my wardrobe choices trashed by old geezers who haven't bought ties since they stopped painting Hula girls on them," I said and nodded thanks at Hazel for putting the surgical instruments on the table where we operate.

"Anyway, who does Air Canada think it is, denying dogs room on their planes? Cats, I can understand because cats weren't meant to travel, weren't meant to do anything for that matter. Cats get born to hang around the house all day and move only when the sunny spot does."

Perley and Harry Charles pretend they don't like cats and it's a pretty convincing act. They always blow their act, though, when they come to visit me and TLC walks over and bats them on the shin to tell them he wants a back rub.

"Anyway, Westjet says dogs are welcome on its flights so they'll pick up all the customers Air Canada will lose when dog owners switch their business."

"You know, to be honest, Perley, in all the years I travelled, I don't think I saw much evidence that dogs were that big a factor in Air Canada's business. I did see dog crates from time to time in airports, and that's how Hank got here from Pennsylvania. But I doubt it's even a percentage of a percentage of the business Air Can does in a year."

"That's not the point. Dogs have always been able to fly and now they can't. It's because they're easterners and easterners are cat people who care more about money and profits than the feelings of dog people."

"Am I to gather that because you arrived first and get to pick the topic for debate that it'll be flying dogs versus cats tonight?" That's the unbreakable rule: the first to arrive gets to pick the first topic and at The Ranchmen's we don't break our own rules.

"It depends. When Harry Charles and Purvis get here, they might have heard something juicier or even newer on CHAT on their way over."

CHAT is the Medicine Hat radio station most of us listen to for important information like the weather. There's also a radio station down in Montana that plays a lot of old country and western stuff from the last century that draws a few listeners from around here. We don't get too many topics for debate from the Montana station unless they get some of those free-trading, free-enterprise American beef ranchers on the radio who want to stop imports of Canadian beef.

We decided not to use up too much of the topic on the chance Harry Charles and Purvis didn't have any suggestions, so we switched over to today's weather and tomorrow's forecast while we waited.

When Purvis and Harry Charles arrived, Purvis launched into the same topic Perley had raised: no dogs flying Air Canada ever again.

"This is a multi-million dollar opportunity," he said, "and we've got a chance to get in early and get rich before anybody else spots it."

Both he and Harry Charles thanked Hazel for her efforts and raised their mugs in unison. Sometimes when I watch these guys, I think of ballet. Not that I've ever been to one, but from what I've heard those dancers are pretty well synchronized too.

"You know that old school bus those folks at the west end of town are going to convert into a motor home some day?" Purvis said. "That's our ticket to fortune. We'll buy it from them and convert it into a bus for dogs. We'll call it The All Hound Bus Line."

"I told Purvis on the way over that he's got the formula down pat," Harry Charles said. "Get the name first because all the rest is just details."

"Except for the profit part and that's where you focus first. And the way I figure it, we could charge 42 cents per kilometre to take a dog from Calgary to anywhere the human is going. If it was Toronto, that'd be what, say 2000 kilometres times 42 cents. What would that work out to in total?" He turned to Harry Charles who closed his eyes so he could see his internal calculator.

"Eight hundred and forty bucks."

"I don't think that's going to cover the cost of a driver, his accommodation, meals and the gasoline," Perley said. "I could be wrong, you might get a guy who wouldn't mind sleeping in the bus with the dog," and he nodded his head in my direction. "But there's still meals and gasoline."

"I said dogs, not dog, Perley. This is big picture stuff. We put 100 dogs on that bus, not one, and we charge each human 42 cents a kilometre. What did you say that would work out to, Harry Charles?"

"Eighty-four thousand bucks."

"And that's just one way. You'd get another $84,000 on the way back. You'd only have to make 10 trips a year to Toronto to get up over a million and that's just one route."

"I told Purvis that ideas like this made Canada the great entrepreneurial nation that it is," Harry Charles told us. "If he can pull this off, they'll build a statue of him somewhere that people can take their dogs to visit."

"I know it's just a detail, Purvis, but there is the scheduling matter. How do you get a dog in a converted school bus to Toronto at the same time the human lands there? That's about a four day drive." Perley leaned back looking like he hoped he hadn't thrown a wrench into Purvis' school bus.

"It's just a matter of scheduling, and that's one of those small picture details that get in the way of big ideas. We'll leave four days before the plane takes off and the dogs will be there waiting for their humans when they touch down in Toronto. Hell, with those profits we could have two drivers going non-stop night and day, except for when the dogs all have to piddle."

"You're way ahead of me on this one, Purvis." Perley was obviously impressed by Purvis' business acumen.

"But we have to be cautious too," Purvis said, "we won't just dive into it without a dry run or two to make sure it all works. I thought of this dry run thing at the same time I thought of having to stop to let the dogs piddle."

"You should write to Stephen Harper and tell him about this idea," I said to Purvis. "Tell him you wouldn't make a final decision until you've made a dry run to see if it works."

"What would that accomplish? The Prime Minister isn't going to invest our tax dollars in a private business."

"No, but he might offer you a chance to do a dry run and get some experience."

"Doing what?"

"Driving the media bus in the next election campaign."

Harry Charles waved at Hazel and pointed at me to indicate I was to be rewarded. "I'll bet you thought of that at exactly the moment Purvis said he'd have to stop the bus to let the dogs piddle."

And God Created Manyberries

When People Get Old

Harry Charles jerked his chin up in greeting as I pulled a chair back from the table to join him for the cocktail hour. He didn't say anything but went on reading a page torn from the Calgary Herald. That's unusual for him; when he wants to save an article he always carefully clips it out with scissors and glues it to a three-hole blank sheet. He has binders full of newspaper clippings going back 40 or 50 years. He also has ancient scrapbooks of clippings dating back to World War One that some long dead old man he knew gave him for safekeeping for posterity.

He still didn't say anything when he handed me the clipping to read. It was about an elderly couple living in a residence in Calgary and how they were going to have to separate. They were both in their 90s and had already lived apart for a period of time because of a lack of accommodation for the elderly. They were reunited at a facility that was now in financial trouble. The story said that it was almost a certainty they would have to be separated again.

"That's about the saddest story I've read in a long time," I said. "Married for 60 plus years and they can't spend their final days together."

"That's the cruellest story you'll ever read" Harry Charles said and he spit the words out.

"What kind of society yanks an old couple apart when the rest of their lives are measured in months, if not weeks or days?"

Harry Charles is one those guys who rarely gets, as he calls it, his dander up. He remains calm and unruffled in crises that send other men spinning. He once explained to me that when he was 10 years old his mother died and his older brother suffered terrible nightmares for several years after they buried her. Because they shared a bed it fell to Harry Charles to talk his brother out of his nightmares. He said it was pretty spooky for a little guy to wake up to his brother screaming that something or somebody was coming to get him. He said he'd hold his brother tight and assure him that he'd hold on to him and not let anybody or anything drag him away. "I think that's when I learned that somebody has to remain calm and in control when everybody else is losing it," he told me.

He told me the story when I was visiting one time and asked about a framed photo he had on the wall over his work desk. It was of his father, Harry Charles and his brothers and sisters taken on the day they buried his mother. It's a very sombre picture and when the context is explained you understand why the young ones look so bewildered and the father so grim. I think a lot of people who survived the great flu epidemic while losing loved ones would have seen their own emotions reflected in that photo.

I guess it could be said that Harry Charles carries his emotions nobly and with discretion.

I looked closely at him and could see the anger in his eyes and disgust on his face.

There was a blast of chilly air when the door opened and Purvis and Perley walked in and came to the table to join us.

Perley saw the newspaper clipping and asked if it was yet another in an endless series on the weirdness of Toronto.

"No, it's a story on why I'll switch my vote to any party but the Conservatives." His anger caught both Purvis and Perley off guard and they sat quietly while Hazel put their mugs down.

"You know that trunk I take when we go hunting?" Harry Charles asked and we all nodded.

"I've been lugging that thing around for nearly 50 years. We used it as our camping trunk when the kids were young and I've been using it ever since to store and carry everything we need. Here, read this." He handed the clipping to Perley. Purvis leaned over to read it at the same time.

When they'd finished, they shook their heads at the sadness of it all.

"That old guy in the picture, his name is Jack, helped me build that trunk. He worked for me in Calgary. I was okay as an amateur carpenter but it takes a little know-how to build a sturdy box. Old Jack there showed me how."

He took the clipping back and carefully folded it and put it in his shirt pocket.

"I'm going to tack this to a wall so I see it every day to remind me never to vote for a Conservative again. If those guys up in Edmonton can't find it in their hearts to do something for the old men and women who served their country so well in war and peace, they don't deserve anybody's vote."

Both Purvis and Perley nodded their agreement. Like Harry Charles both are Conservative through and through and have probably wished they could vote early and often in past elections as long as it was for the Conservative.

"Here we are in the richest province in Canada," Harry Charles continued, "and we can't find the wherewithal or the heart to let an old couple spend their last days together. You guys tell me where's the Alberta heart or so-called advantage in that." It wasn't put as a question that required an answer.

Later, when Harry Charles and I were walking toward our respective homes with a wet heavy snow falling, he stopped and turned to me. He had tears in his eyes.

"I've heard these young Conservative bullshit artists talk about how business and the markets are better than governments when it comes to helping people live better and more fulfilled lives. And I've heard them prattle on about the Alberta advantage. I'd like to take one of old Jack's hunting socks and stuff it down their throats."

That was the first time ever I heard Harry Charles swear.

"You should go home and write one of your letters to the editor," he said. "But this time send it."

The Manyberries
Flag Ceremony

"I need some help down at the Post Office." I had been engrossed in a crossword puzzle that Four-Eyed Tom had left behind and hadn't looked up when Perley entered. Four-Eyed buys whole books of crossword puzzles and has accumulated a stack of them nearly 10 feet high since he retired. Each time he finishes a book he takes the one on the bottom out to read, puts the finished copy on top of the stack and begins working on a new edition. Four-Eyed figures he's enriching his vocabulary to well beyond university graduate levels.

Harry Charles says Four-Eyed doesn't have much ambition if that level satisfies him and that he should really aim for levels achieved by high school graduates 50 years ago. Besides, he'll add, Four-Eyed Tom doesn't talk a whole lot to anybody so he really doesn't need a grand vocabulary.

The reason I was so engrossed was that I was stalled on "What comes after Niagara?" I had written down peninsula, wine and region and couldn't think of anything else.

"What comes after Niagara?" I asked Perley.

"Falls," he answered. "How long have you been here?"

"Oh, about four, no five, glasses of wine."

"Okay, you can hold the ladder and I'll go up and do it. It won't take long."

"What won't take long and what ladder?" I have reservations about helping people if it means serious manual labour and it has been my experience that ladders are very often connected with manual labour.

"I need to go up on the roof of the Post Office and lower the flag to half-mast and I thought I would get you to do it while I held the ladder. But I can do it because I don't want you wandering around up there with that much wine on your mind."

"Why do you need to lower the flag?" We only do that on Remembrance Day or when somebody in town we all like passes away.

"Albert died last night and we have to mark his passing."

There is only one Albert, or was only one Albert, and he was Sanders' dog, a mixed breed of Border Collie and Labrador. Sanders got him from a farmer who swore the father was a Lab that belonged to a rich oilman from Calgary who came down in October to hunt pheasants. The farmer claimed, Sanders told us, that his Border Collie bitch happened to be feeling amorous one weekend when the hunter was there and the Labrador was quite accommodating. Sanders said he couldn't pass up a mutt whose father was a $2000 born-and-bred Labrador from the east coast of the United States, and besides, the farmer was giving the pups away.

"I didn't know you lowered the flag for dogs." Lowering the flag is a very big deal in Manyberries, not like Ottawa where the flag goes up and down on the Peace Tower like a yo-yo. Purvis once said the flag was lowered so often that if some politician's pet rabbit caught a cold, they'd have it at half-mast in a minute.

"Well, we lower it when somebody we all like passes away, and we've always had a tradition of lowering the flag for the odd dog that died or even the occasional cat if the cat had lots of personality and character. And Albert was as goofy a dog as you ever met and gave some of us a lot of laughs over his 18 years."

"Yeah, I have to admit I got a few chuckles out of his antics." Albert was the most flatulent and had the loosest bowels of all the dogs in town. People said it was because Sanders always fed Albert table scraps and the Sanders ate a lot of cabbage and corn from their garden. When Albert would accompany Sanders on a visit to the Ranchmen's the other dogs waiting for their owners would watch to see where Albert was going to lie down and then move so they'd be upwind of him.

"Anyway, I want to lower the flag for Albert and there's nobody around to help except you."

"Okay." I sort of sighed so Perley would know that this would require no small effort on my part to drive the 300 yards over to the Post Office with him and to hold the ladder.

I waved to Hazel to let her know I would be back to have another glass of wine and to tackle Four-Eyed's crossword puzzle book.

The Manyberries Post Office is really just a small, squarish building, about 12 feet high, with a lot of mail boxes in it. For a flagpole, Harry Charles cut, skinned and polished a diamond willow and attached the appropriate hardware, while Purvis came up with a patio umbrella stand that he screwed to the roof, although they did need to jam in some shims to hold it upright. Finding a flag that wasn't too big or too small was a challenge but the kids in the elementary art class painted one just the right size. That flag is a symbol of pride for Manyberries because so many people invested so much in it.

As we pulled away from the Ranchmen's, Purvis and Harry Charles arrived in Purvis' old pickup. Hank the Weimaraner was in the back with ears waving in the wind and grinning like he'd just had a good day.

"I wondered where he was when I left the house," I commented to Perley.

"Well, Harry Charles and Purvis decided to go out and scout for birds and asked Hank if he wanted to go along. I didn't think they'd be back this early or I would have waited for somebody sober to go up on the roof while I held the ladder."

"I don't get it," I said. "Here they are raising a fuss in Ottawa over when the flag should be lowered and here we are going to the mail box building to lower the flag for a dog, admittedly a dog everybody liked, but still a dog."

"After you've been here a few more years, you'll get it." He stayed in first gear all the way to the job site because sometimes his old clunker loses track of where its second gear is.

When he got the flag lowered and the ladder back on top of the car, we decided we had better go back to the Ranchmen's. I had to settle my tab and maybe have another one or two and both of us wanted to know if Harry Charles, Purvis and Hank had come across any birds on their scouting trip.

"Tell me something," I said as we crawled along in first gear. "If Hank died would you lower the flag?"

"In a heartbeat," Perley said. "Everybody likes Hank and there'd be an uproar if we didn't."

"And I suppose you'd lower it for the jackrabbit that lives under the trailer over on the edge of town?"

"Well yeah, of course we would. All the dogs in town have taken a shine to that jackrabbit and never chase him anymore. They'd put up a howl if we didn't recognize his passing."

"Okay, that's nice to know. Tell me this, if I died, would you lower the flag for me?"

"I think we'd probably have to have a sitdown and talk about it," he answered. "Thing of it is, lowering the flag is a very solemn occasion and folks around here take it pretty seriously. They don't want it to become so common that it cheapens the symbolism of the ceremony."

And God Created Manyberries

Fanny's Flames of Illiteracy

"Man, are they ever upset over in Regina," Purvis said after he settled in his chair and his two mugs were on the table. "My sister-in-law Fanny swears she'll never, ever, vote Conservative again."

"I recall Fanny saying she had never voted for any party but the New Democrats last time she and Bert were here for a visit," Harry Charles responded. "In fact, she told us her father and grandfather had never voted for any party but the CCF and even after that when it renamed itself the NDP, and what was good enough for them was good enough for her."

"Strictly speaking that's true, but she was wavering when they elected Jack Layton as their leader. She hates moustaches, calls them mouse stashes."

"Well, one person's sense of humour is another person's wince," Harry Charles said, "and nobody ever wrote a book on the humour of Saskatchewan."

""So what has set the political pot boiling this time, Purvis?" Perley asked. "The Canadian Wheat Board? Or did someone tell her that free health care might not be sustainable?"

It has been our observation that over in Saskatchewan the folks are convinced that somehow taxpayer-funded health care is free and has been ever since Tommy Douglas told them it would be.

"Neither," Purvis said. "This time it's about literacy and federal funding. Seems the new government in Ottawa is cutting funding to groups that are trying to stamp out illiteracy and Fanny belongs to one of those groups. Man, she burned up the telephone line telling me the country will be going to hell because people won't be able to read the road signs."

"Well, it seems a shame that they're yanking money from people who are out there trying to teach people to read," Perley sympathized. "Although I can't figure out why the schools didn't teach them when they had them under lock and key. You know, and it's just my opinion, we pay the teachers to teach and if they did their job there wouldn't be any kid leaving school without knowing how to read."

"But it's not just people who were born here, Perley, you've got a lot of immigrants coming in who need help and if they can't read, they won't be able to operate." Harry Charles had a lot of experience in his working days with immigrants he hired who couldn't read. He once said they were just as smart as whips and could do all the jobs except those that required reading or writing so they often got stuck at the bottom doing the grunt work.

"Anyway, strictly speaking, Fanny and her group weren't actually teaching people how to read. They called themselves advocates for literacy and were promoting literacy rather than actually teaching it."

"So the government cut their funding and now they can't hire people to go in there and teach people how to read?"

"No. Strictly speaking, they didn't hire teachers. They used the government money to get out and around and tell people how important it is that everybody learns to read. The money from Ottawa was to cover expenses, like for travel and accommodation when they went out to speak to groups like Rotary or the curling clubs and for fund-raising."

"Fund-raising? If they were getting money from the government, why would they have to raise funds?"

'Well, every year they have a big gala dinner to celebrate literacy and they use part of the government money to drive around to tell local businesses they should contribute and buy tickets to the dinner. That's pretty expensive, the gasoline, maybe staying in motels if they go out of town, buying lunch for donors and so on."

"Wait a minute," Harry Charles said. "Are you saying they spend the government money raising more money so they can go out and make speeches about how important literacy is? And nobody ever actually sits down and teaches people to read?"

"Well, they have office rent to pay, telephone bills, a new computer and they take turns managing the office and you can't expect them to sit in an office all day as managers without some compensation. And they pay out of their own pockets for the new dresses they have to buy every year for the big gala dinner."

Harry Charles held up his right hand with four fingers extended as a signal for a reload of the table. "Wonder how many groups there are like that across Canada?"

And God Created Manyberries

"Fanny said there are hundreds of them and they're all going to have to shut down."

"Geez, that'll run into the millions, I'll bet. Wonder what the government will do with all that money it saves?"

"Fanny says they're talking about using it to hire people to teach people how to read and write."

"She can't object to that, can she? If more people who can't read are actually taught to read, doesn't that accomplish what she and her group were advocating? She should take a measure of pride in that small victory."

"She doesn't see it that way, nor does Bert. He says that the literacy thing kept her out of the dealership telling his sales guys they should be washing the used cars when they aren't dealing with customers."

"I hope she doesn't start suing the government for breach of contract," Perley said.

"Nope, they have a new plan and Fanny says she thinks they can get even more money from Ottawa for an even more important advocacy campaign. She says they're going to change their name to Citizens for a Bilingual Saskatchewan and apply for federal funding to get everybody in the province speaking French."

"That'll be a tough sell in Saskatchewan," Harry Charles said, shaking his head in doubt.

"That's not the point, Saskatchewan doesn't figure into it at all. What counts is how easy it'll be to sell it in Ottawa and Fanny thinks it'll be a cakewalk. And Bert says he's behind her all the way and even offering to pay her fare to Ottawa so she can make the pitch in person. That'll keep her busy if she gets the grant and give him more time to play poker with his sales guys between customers."

The Baby Boom

"What are your thoughts on polygamy?" Harry Charles asked as he pulled back a chair to join me for the cocktail hour.

"I haven't thought about that since I was, oh maybe about 18 or 21 and it wasn't thinking about it so much as it was fantasizing about it."

"Maybe it's time to give it serious consideration," he said and waved at Perley and Purvis, who had just come through the front door of the Ranchmen's.

"You know, one of the reasons I prefer Manyberries over Ottawa is the variety of topics up for discussion at any given time. Down there they stick to two topics, except in the warm months when all they talk about is when and where their next golf game will be. The other two are when the next election will be and which politician is gaining or losing weight."

Harry Charles handed me a newspaper clipping as Perley and Purvis pulled back their chairs and waved at Hazel at the bar.

The clipping was a column by William Johnson on the success of Mario Dumont in the last Quebec election. HC had underlined the last three paragraphs with a red ink pen and had obviously used a ruler.

I scanned down to the underlined paragraphs and read that Mario Dumont, according to Johnson, was proposing $100 a week for each Quebec child under six not in subsidized day care and a $5000 cash bonus for a third or subsequent child. I did a quick mental calculation and understood why it was underlined. I wish Mario Dumont had been around when my own kids were young. That would have given me $200 a week, which is about what I was earning back then, which meant my annual income would have doubled without a whole lot of

And God Created Manyberries

effort or burning ambition. And that $5000 for a third kid would likely have prompted some second thoughts about the ideal family size.

"So this young guy Mario Dumont in Quebec is proposing that families be paid 100 bucks a week for every kid under six and that parents who have a third child get a cash bonus of $5000," he told Perley and Purvis, who were looking impatiently in Hazel's direction.

"Cripes, that would have meant 300 bucks a week for me and 10 grand for the other two," Purvis said. "I probably could have retired earlier."

"This could be a windfall for Manyberries if we passed a by-law permitting polygamy," Harry Charles said. "I was just asking the young guy," and he jerked a thumb at me, "what his thoughts are on polygamy. But, as should have been expected, he turned the topic back to what people talk about in Ottawa."

"Well, what are your thoughts?" Perley asked Harry Charles.

"I was thinking if we had a few energetic young men and each had a few energetic young wives, there'd be government cash falling on Manyberries like poplar leaves."

"You don't actually believe in polygamany, do you?" Purvis wondered.

"It's polygamy, Purvis and no, I always thought it was unfair to the women, but in the interests of a sound financial future for Manyberries, I'd be willing to reconsider."

"I see your point," Perley said, and took out his wire spiral pocket notebook and pencil. "Let's take four young men, each with four young wives as a starter." He licked the pencil tip and began jotting down figures.

"So what's new?" Hazel asked as she unloaded a tray. "Are you adding up your vast assets again, Perley?"

"No, we're thinking about introducing polygamy to Manyberries," Harry Charles told her. "There could be a cash windfall in it."

"What do they call it when a woman has several husbands? Now, if you want to talk about that, I'll pull up a chair and join you." Hazel is a little beyond what you might call a woman of a certain age but word around town is her husband looks pretty tired a lot of mornings.

"This is cash for kids," Harry Charles explained. "In Quebec if a woman had enough kids she'd probably generate enough cash in a few short years to buy a new pickup."

"Been there, done that. If you guys want anything important, just wave." Hazel filled her tray with empties and returned to the bar.

"I don't know about this," Purvis said. "Not that I never thought about polygamany, or whatever you call it, because I did. But it's against the law, except if you live in a group and the government decides to ignore what you're doing."

"When did you ever think about polygamy, Purvis?"

"Oh, back when I was 18 or maybe 21. But it wasn't so much as to whether it was right or wrong. It was just, you know, what a young man thinks about when he's out in the bush on a drill rig for three months straight without a visit to town."

"It's pretty complicated arithmetic," Perley said, looking up from his calculations. "But a preliminary estimate supports what you say, Harry Charles. There'd be a whole fleet of new pickups in Manyberries if we got this Mario Dumont guy to come out here and run for mayor."

"This would be a very different country if we'd had forward looking politicians like young Dumont running for office back in the 30s and 40s," Harry Charles said. "A lot of guys our age could have been driving Cadillacs before we retired."

A Manyberries Compass

Out here on the prairies you don't need a compass to navigate. There's no bush, no forest and nothing standing in the way to hide the rising or setting of the sun. If you know the sun comes up in the east and goes down in the west, you have a pretty good handle on which of the two remaining directions is north or south.

If you look to the south, you can see the mountains in Montana; if you're close enough that you have to tilt your head back to see the mountaintops, you can safely conclude that you are now *in* Montana.

If you are a little fretful about getting lost on the prairie, just park your vehicle on a high hill when you go walking. To locate it, all you have to do is climb a few hills until you are on one high enough to see your vehicle when you get to the top. You'll be able to see it five miles away when it's parked on a high short grass hill and you can't mistake it for a rock or clump of brush because there are no rocks that big out here and no brush higher than your knees.

It isn't that way in the foothills or on the eastern slopes of the Rocky Mountains where there's a lot of heavily wooded areas. You can get lost there pretty easily if you don't have a compass. I can get lost there even when I do have a compass because I always forget to get a bearing before I head into the bush when I'm hunting.

That was something that was explained to me many times by Harry Charles. He would take out his compass and tell me to get mine out of my pocket. Then, after I scraped off the melted chocolate bar and flakes of tobacco, he would commence the lesson.

"First you get a bearing and look well ahead to some object in the distance. It might be an unusual tree or a rock or maybe a bush. You look at your compass and see that the object is west or northwest and you head for it. You just have to remember when you want to turn around that you will be headed east or southeast to get you right back to within feet of where you started."

"That's great," I'd say, "but what if your compass isn't working? What if it got demagnetized or something?"

"Always trust your compass," he'd say. "The compass never lies and your instincts do. It's like life – you have your inside compass and your outside instincts. The compass says give and the instincts say take. You can get turned around so quick, if you don't believe your compass you're going to be lost for a long, long time and then you might get bush-spooked and that will kill you."

Then, to drive his point home, he'd tell me about people getting lost in the bush in Ontario. "Some of them don't realize they're lost until they pass the same rock or recognizable tree for the third time. When that happens, they get nervous and start walking a little more quickly. When they pass that same object for the sixth time, they start running. After that, unless somebody intercepts them or they somehow change their natural pace, it's damn near going to be all over for that poor soul because he'll just keep making bigger and bigger circles and always coming back to the same place."

I asked him what he meant by changing pace and he said that most people have one stride a little longer with one leg than the other. If the right stride is longer than the left, the person walking will be forced into a right-turning circle even if that person thinks he or she is walking a straight line. At least that's what I think he said. He might have said a longer right stride would turn you left. I thought of, and then rejected, the idea of going into the bush to see whether my stride is longer left or right.

"What's bush-spooked?" I asked when he gave me my first compass lesson.

"It's when a person panics and starts running. The old boys used to say when somebody had been lost a few days, they might see a search party but being bush-spooked will hide from their rescuers."

"I don't think I'd get bush-spooked," I said. "I'd have my gun, some chocolate bars, matches if I wanted a fire, and my water bottle."

A few years later I was up north in Alberta working for a grain-buying outfit and saving money for my higher education when I was called out to search for my first lost person. She was an old Ukrainian grandmother who had wandered away from the farm. When the town whistle blew, the senior agent called me and said we'd go down to find out what the trouble was. When we learned they were calling for searchers we joined the caravan heading for the farm.

There were close to 50 searchers gathered and we were organized into lines of about 12 or 14 and sent off in all four directions.

My line was about 200 yards into the bush when I heard a high-pitched voice right at my feet. I must have jumped six feet in the air because I had dreadful visions of finding the old lady dead. But she was more than alive, huddled up there in the dark against a poplar tree, and I had stepped on her foot.

Two of the boys who could speak Ukrainian picked her up and carried her back to the farm and everybody went home happy.

Next time we were hunting, I told Harry Charles about that search and he said the old lady had done what was smart. She had sat herself down and waited for people to find her.

I told Harry Charles it had made me feel pretty good, being the one who found her on a pretty cold October night. "Helping somebody should always make you feel good," he said. "There's no better way to feel good than by helping people or doing someone a kindness. You were using the other compass, the one that isn't covered with bits of chocolate and flakes of tobacco."

"But I don't know if I could sit still and just wait for somebody to come and find me," I said. "What if you sat there and they passed a half mile away? You could be out there all winter, waiting for somebody to come and get you."

He told me about his father and his uncles Peter, Tinny, Jack and Charlie. These tough old coots were born between about 1870 and 1882 and were experienced woodsmen. They had all told him if he ever got lost in the bush just to sit down and wait for somebody to come and get him. He said he still thought that way in the bush: that his father, Peter, Tinny, Jack and Charlie were with him.

But he told me he had listened and then said to them, "But if I'm lost and you don't know where I am, how will you find me?"

They told him not to worry; if he got lost at least one of them would be there to bring him out.

"Yeah, well, if I get lost, I'll just sit down and wait for you to come and bring me out," I said.

"That's a good idea," he replied. "And you won't be lonesome because my dad, Peter, Tinny, Jack and Charlie will sit with you to keep you company while I'm finding you. And if they're not all with you, a couple will be with me, showing me where you are."

Sometimes these days, like when the planes hit the World Trade Center, or most days when the news is grim and I wonder what the world's coming to, I pretend I'm lost. I sit down and sit still and wait for the sound of Harry Charles' footsteps. And I enjoy the company of Harry Charles, Tinny, Peter, Jack and Charlie while I'm waiting.

Haunting Manyberries

It was a late October evening when I walked into the Ranchmen's to find only Purvis at our regular table. I should explain that the cocktail hour in October gets pushed back because it is hunting season and the regulars find it impossible to be there for the usual 4:30-6:30. By the regulars I mean Harry Charles, Perley, and Purvis when he isn't too busy doing business to go hunting. The cocktail hour for some starts at about the same time the Ranchmen's opens and ends when it closes.

"The old boys must have gone further afield than usual," I said as I pulled out a chair, "or had a flat tire or got stuck somewhere."

"Nah, they went up to Medicine Hat to get their Halloween supplies," Purvis told me. "They have to get a couple of mountains of treats for the kids so they drove north to hunt early and continued north on up there to go shopping."

"I wonder how many of those of treats actually get to the kids and how much those two old hounds save for themselves?"

"Oh, that'd never happen. They always buy two mountains, one each for them and the other for the kids. They'd never short-change the little ones, anymore than they'd short-change themselves on Halloween treats," Purvis chuckled.

"I recall when my kids were young and still tricking and treating that Harry Charles and Perley had bagged their candies and wrote their names on them so people, parents I guess, would know where they came from."

"Yeah, that was quite a few years ago. Harry Charles had read a newspaper story about some monster putting nasty things in the kids' bags one Halloween and he wanted to make sure the parents knew his treats were safe. The two of them said they would have

And God Created Manyberries

preferred to track the son of a bitch down and hang him but Toronto is too big and too long a drive." Purvis waved at the bar for another round.

"Were you here when we had what they call The Night Halloween Froze Over?"

"No," I replied, "can't say as I remember anything like that."

Purvis waited until the two new mugs were settled comfortably on the table. "Geez, it must have been 15 years ago," he said. "A norther blew in, a real howling, freezing norther that came down early and caught us all by surprise the day before Halloween. With the wind factored in, it was nearly 60 below and you couldn't see halfway across the road in the blizzard. That was the year the parents decided to postpone Halloween until it blew over. Boy, I'll tell you the kids were disappointed. But there was just no way you'd want little ones out there in that weather so the parents promised that as soon as it got warm they could go out trick and treating."

"Why didn't they just have everybody gather at the school and do it there?"

"Well, that was proposed by somebody but Harry Charles and Perley argued against. It was Harry Charles who said Halloween was a magical night for the kids and part of the magic was going door to door and scaring the bejabbers out of people. They both said it wouldn't be fair to the little ones to deprive them of that so instead of the school, they should just postpone it. They said it didn't matter what night Halloween was supposed to be, what mattered was the kids should have a real Halloween."

"And folks bought that argument? In some city neighbourhoods they do it at community halls so the kids will be safe."

"That's what some people think but Harry Charles said some cities aren't like Manyberries and if they aren't safe here, there's no place left on earth where they will be."

"So how long did it take before they had their Halloween?"

"Oh, not even a week. A Chinook blew in, it was like an autumn evening and they had as good a Halloween as they ever had. In fact, they had two Halloweens that year because of Harry Charles and Perley."

"You mean the kids stayed home and ate all the treats their parents had bought for other kids?"

"No, like I told my grandkids, if they ate the candy we had for other kids, what would we give them when they came to the door on whatever night we decided to hold Halloween? They saw the logic in that and called their friends to get them to promise not to eat the treats they had at home and they'd do the same."

"So how did they have two Halloweens that year?"

"Well, Harry Charles and Perley got together and decided to give them a temporary Halloween. Perley bagged the treats they had for the kids and got dressed up. Harry Charles had an old King Kong mask and got Irene to glue horse hair on some gloves so he'd have hairy paws. Perley fashioned himself as a headless man and carried a pumpkin under one arm for a head. The two of them went door to door in that god-awful weather and gave every kid a bag of treats, some of the adults too."

"So that's how Manyberries had two Halloweens in one year. And you called that The Night Halloween Froze Over?"

"Yep, and the second one that year was as big a success as any other we've had and it didn't matter at all to the kids what night it was."

"So Harry Charles and Perley had to make another trip to Medicine Hat to get more treats for the kids when they finally did go door to door?"

"No, they used their own personal mountains. Perley said it was okay because if they drove up to Medicine Hat within a week or two of Halloween, all the candies and treats would be on sale for a lot less so they could buy even bigger mountains for themselves."

Purvis leaned back in his chair and took a swallow. "The parents all got together and gave each of them a bottle of the best rum money can buy to warm them up after being out in the cold that night." He took another swallow and leaned forward.

"It must make for a good morning when you wake up smiling and wondering what excitement the day will bring. I remember feeling that as a kid myself. You know, I wish I had as much of the little kid in me as those two old geezers have."

　　　　　　　　And God Created Manyberries

Where the Dinosaurs Roam

Perley and Harry Charles arrived earlier than usual for the cocktail hour and I asked where Purvis was. It was late February and that's a slow time in Manyberries. About all there is to do is gather daily for the cocktail hour and wait for spring.

"He'll be along shortly and he's got something for us," Perley replied. He made a beckoning wave at Four-Eyed Tom, who was at his crossword puzzle table reading one of his completed books. When Four-Eyed had settled into his chair Perley asked him what he knew about dinosaurs.

"I can't pronounce their names but I could probably spell some of them if you said them slowly," was the reply.

"Well, at least you know more than I do, so that'll come in handy," Perley told him.

"What's this all about, this dinosaur stuff?" I asked.

"Wait til Purvis gets here," Harry Charles said and waved at Hazel to let her know cocktail hour could commence at our table anytime it was convenient for her.

"But I will tell you this," he said, "Purvis has a new project and he wants all of us to get in on it."

Harry Charles and Perley are always encouraging Purvis when he gets a new idea or develops a new scheme or project. It helps to pass the time between hunting seasons. As Harry Charles says, "how often do you get to witness a catastrophe from beginning through middle to the end?"

When Purvis arrived he was carrying a gunny sack that clanked, which he dropped on the floor. He leaned over and pulled out what appeared to be a primitive weapon which might have been fashioned by some ancient Iron Age warrior.

He laid it on the table and said he had seven more just like it in the sack. "It's a pailingtologist tool," he informed us.

"That'd be palaeontologist, Purvis," Harry Charles corrected him.

"Whatever, doesn't matter, as long as they work – and they will, because I've already given one of them a test run. My son helped me put them together in his shop at the ranch."

"Looks like a railroad spike," Four-Eyed Tom observed. "Or a hand-to-hand combat weapon."

Purvis picked it up and fondled it. "That's what it is. I found a box of railroad spikes years ago and always knew they'd come in handy. So we welded one spike to another and now we can go looking for dinosaurs."

"Indiana Jones will be rolling over in his grave," I said.

"Who's Indiana Jones?" Purvis asked.

"Nobody you'd know," I replied, "just a guy who used to hunt for old stuff, stuff that was even older than you guys."

Purvis looked at Harry Charles and Perley. "Did you guys tell these two what this is all about?"

"Not a word, we just said you had a project and you were going to generously invite us all to get involved."

"Did you guys hear about Cecil Nesmo?" Purvis asked Four-Eyed and me. We shook our heads.

Cecil Nesmo is rancher whose family has been in the Manyberries area for a couple of generations.

"They've named a dinosaur after him," Purvis informed us, "a dinosaur they dug up on his ranch."

"Why would they go and do that?" Four-Eyed wondered. "Cecil isn't that old so why would they go and liken him to a dinosaur?"

"No no no, they did it to honour him because they found the dinosaur on his ranch." Purvis pulled a slip of paper from his pocket. "I've got it written down here. I don't know how to say it so I'll spell it. It's Alberta and then c-e-r-a-t-o-p-s nesmoi. That "nesmoi" is for Cecil."

"Let me jump ahead and guess what you have in mind," I offered. "I have this nightmarish picture of five men with primitive pickaxes sweating in a pit or on a sidehill on Cecil's ranch, slaving away under an unrelenting sun looking for dinosaur bones. Is that about right?"

"You don't sound very enthusiastic," Harry Charles chided me. "Which is not surprising considering some manual labour is required."

"How hard can it be to hack away at dirt until you find a fossil?

And you probably look for bones sticking out of the ground and then start picking at them." Perley took a long swallow and waved at Hazel to recharge the mugs. "It's not as if you'd be walking all over the ranch digging holes at random."

"Tell you what I'll do," I said, "I'll go along and keep the beer cooler in the shade and bring you guys one for every gallon of sweat you lose. And I'll bring along my patio umbrella for shade when you break for lunch or refreshments."

"If you don't dig you don't get a dinosaur named after you," Purvis warned.

"There's no way the guys who name dinosaurs are going to name one and then put Tom after it," Four-Eyed Tom told him. "So I'll go along with him," he pointed at me, "and keep the beer cooler in the shade and if you get somebody else to help you, give him my railroad spike pickaxe."

Harry Charles cleared his throat, leaned forward and dropped what appeared to be a rock on the table. "If you guys did decide to join the dig and lower yourselves to a little manual labour, you might get something like this as a souvenir."

I knew what it was: a fossilized oyster I found up around Drumheller one time when we were hunting mule deer. It was lying on the surface of a gently sloped side hill in the badlands. I saw it when I sat down to rest halfway to the top. I carried it up to where Harry Charles had been waiting patiently for me to finish the climb. Sure he's 30 years older than me, but he wasn't carrying as many chocolate bars. I gave him the oyster to carry.

"What is it?" Perley asked. "Looks like a fossilized horse bun."

"It's an oyster," Harry Charles explained. "Probably as old as that dinosaur they named after Cecil." He passed it to Four-Eyed Tom to examine. "I call it Oyster Harry Charles, sort of like Oysters Rockefeller, but those aren't fossils."

"I'd be happy if I found a clam and named it Clam Perley," Perley said.

"Well, I want a dinosaur," Purvis told us. "And I'll leave it to the scientific guys to figure out what to call it, provided they work my name into it somehow."

"So, when do we go, Purvis? I'm not interested in digging through snow and then dirt so I guess it'll be May?" Harry Charles was, as usual, pushing Purvis and encouraging him. The more he pushed, the sooner he'd be able to witness whatever catastrophe awaited.

"May will be good," Purvis agreed. "The snow will be gone, the frost out of the ground and not as much risk of getting the truck stuck in the mud."

"That's not nearly enough time to get all the necessary permits from the government," Harry Charles said and waved at Hazel to give her advance warning that refills would be needed soon. "I think you'd better plan on digging a year or two from now."

"Permits? What permits? We'll just ask Cecil if we can dig a few holes on his ranch and promise to fill them in if we don't find any dinosaurs."

"Well, there's a little hitch here, I'm afraid, and that's permits. It's against the law to go digging for dinosaurs without government permission and without experts to supervise."

"Who the hell needs a permit and experts to dig holes?" Purvis was edging up to his indignant "government interferes in everything too much" rant, which is always most entertaining.

"That's just the way it is, Purvis. They'll track you down, serve you with warrants and take you to court and sue you for your upper plate if you go digging for dinosaurs without permission."

Purvis sat back and sipped his beer and you could see he was thinking there must be something he could salvage out of all his preparation and planning.

He turned to Four-Eyed Tom. "You said these things look like primitive hand-to-hand combat weapons. Would you be interested in trying to sell them to tourists as weapons the Indians fashioned out of spikes when the first rail tracks were laid across the prairie?"

"Sure, shouldn't be too much of a challenge, if they're from Toronto," Four-Eyed said. "Not after I explain how the Indians had their own mobile welding shops."

Santa Visits Manyberries

We were sitting in the Ranchmen's in late December celebrating Harry Charles' birthday when Perley walked in and sat down and sighed deeply. When Perley sighs deeply you know he's got something worrying him and you have to be polite and ask him what's on his mind.

"Christmas mailbag getting too heavy for you, Perley?" I asked. "A guy your age should recruit a volunteer helper if the load's too much so you don't wind up with a bad back over the Christmas season."

There are two things that will make Perley sit up straight and one is to suggest he's maybe getting on in years. The other is that he might want to have somebody along to share the Christmas cheer he gets by the jarful as he makes his Christmas delivery rounds.

"No, and I'll still be delivering mail when you can't boost yourself out of your recliner to walk 300 yards over here to the Ranchmen's because of all those cigarettes you smoke." Perley is about 40 years older than me and is a pipe and cigar man.

"It's my grandsons," he said, finally getting around to the topic that was troubling him. "They're suspicious about Santa Claus and hinting that maybe we're making up all those stories about them having to be good all year round if they want him to visit their house."

Perley's grandsons are five, six and eight years old and that's a terrible age to be at around Christmas time. The older kids won't come right out and say it, but they drop hints about the existence of Santa Claus and plant seeds of doubt among the believers. Most of us can remember the panic we felt when we started to wonder if what our parents said about Santa might not be bang on true. You could depend on Santa because he had magic and if there was no Santa there was the risk, the real and unthinkable risk, that only you and your only-human parents might know what you wanted for Christmas. Of course parents could be used as a conduit to Santa but it was better to rely on your thoughts making their way out across the prairie and on up to the North Pole where Santa would magically pick them up and add your list to his list. Parents are pretty dependable people but boy, you just don't want to take any chances at Christmas.

"Well, it happens to every kid when they reach that age," Harry Charles said, "but it doesn't take a whole lot of effort to put them back in the true believer's camp."

Harry Charles was always considered one of the wise men of Manyberries and could most times be relied on to find a solution to any problem. Sometimes he'd just tell the person with the problem that he or she didn't really have a problem and that would be all it would take to solve it.

"I can remember when I was a kid and my own seeds of doubt were planted and how my uncles kept me in the Santa believer's camp," he said.

"Perley, if you want them to keep the magic, we can come up with a plan guaranteed to make them believe in Santa Claus just as strongly as the rest of us."

"Is it gonna take a lot of work?" I asked. I never minded getting involved in some of Harry Charles' elaborate schemes and plans when it was for the kids but as the youngest of the bunch, the heavy lifting and footwork always seem to fall on my side of the table.

"Nope, not at all," Harry Charles reassured me. "I believe it's your turn to buy me my next birthday drink and I can lay out my plan before Hazel gets here with it."

Seems that when Harry Charles was about seven years old, he began to have those very same doubts about Santa Claus. That would have been in 1914 and his uncles came to the rescue. Seventy years later and thousands of miles away, that same solution was brought to bear in Manyberries.

Harry Charles was born on December 21st so we had very little time to execute the plan to convert Perley's three grandsons back into true believers before old Claus was due to visit.

The next night Harry Charles went over to Perley's, where it had been arranged the grandsons would be visiting. He hauled out a paper sack and said he'd found the strangest thing in his backyard. He spilled the contents out into his hand and let Perley and the grandsons have a look.

And God Created Manyberries

"What do you think it is, Perley?"

Perley peered at the round pellets in Harry Charles' hand and scratched his head. "I don't know, sort of looks like rabbit poop but rabbits don't poop anywhere near that big."

"That's what I was thinking, but for rabbits to poop this big they'd have to be as big as Three-Eyed Tom, and he's the biggest dog anybody ever saw."

The grandsons, fascinated by poop, drew closer and looked at the thumb-sized objects. They were smaller than horse buns, which all three had thrown at each other many times, so they were able to recognize the similarity in texture.

"Now here's the other thing," Harry Charles told Perley. "I found tracks like I've never seen before in my backyard and while they looked like deer tracks, they were way too big for any deer you find around here."

"Do you think they might have been antelope tracks?" Perley asked.

"Nope, antelope have pretty delicate hooves and these were a lot wider. Wide enough for the animal, whatever it was, to make its way across deep snow, it appeared to me."

"Reindeer," the eight-year-old whispered. "Reindeer have to walk across snow when they're not flying."

"Nah, couldn't be reindeer, they're a northern animal, and they'd never drift this far south. Besides they couldn't live on sagebrush and prairie short grass," Perley said.

"Santa Claus has reindeer and they can fly and maybe they were flying over and had a poop on Harry Charles' house," said the six-year-old.

"They'd better not poop on my house," Harry Charles said, "or I'll haul out my old 12 gauge Ithaca and blast them out of the sky."

"Oh, don't shoot the reindeer," the five-year-old said. "Santa wouldn't be able to fly around the world if you killed his reindeer."

"Well, I found these in the backyard and didn't check the roof, so maybe they were polite about where they pooped," Harry Charles relented.

"Come to think of it," Perley said, "when I was coming back last night from the Ranchmen's and your birthday party, I heard a strange swooshing sound, almost like a huge flock of geese going over without any honking."

Well, it's a mystery to me," Harry Charles shrugged, putting the pellets back in the paper sack. "Do you guys want to take these home to show your Mom and Dad?"

The three grandsons nodded and he handed the sack to the oldest.

I'll walk you guys home so your gramps can get lots of sleep before he starts making his Christmas delivery rounds tomorrow."

Along the north side of Perley's yard there's a 10-foot-high hedge he planted as a windbreak and as they stood on his porch saying goodnight, the five-year-old spotted movement on the other side.

"Look," he said, "look at that," pointing his finger in the direction of the hedge.

"What is it?" Perley asked, peering into the darkness. "I can't see anything."

"It's somebody standing there, looking at us," said the eight-year-old.

"I believe you're right," Harry Charles said, "Perley, you should thin that hedge out in the spring so we can see through it better."

"To hell with trimming, I'm gonna get my shotgun," Perley said, "and give this peeping tom a bum full of bird shot."

"No, no, Gramps," the six-year-old said, "he's wearing red and I can see a beard."

"I never trusted anybody with a beard," Harry Charles told them. "Perley, get the shotgun."

"No, no, no, Gramps," the five-year-old was almost crying. "It's Santa Claus and he's hiding behind the bush, watching us."

"Do ya think?" Perley paused, "do ya really think it could be Santa Claus?"

"Geez, could be," said Harry Charles, "he's just standing there staring back at us. We know he scouts ahead before Christmas and could be we've caught him red-handed on a reconnaissance of Manyberries. Boy, I'll tell you, I'm sure glad I've been pretty good for the last few weeks."

All of a sudden, the mysterious figure turned and trotted out of sight. They could hear his boots crunching on the frozen ground until there was only the silence of the dark night and the quick breathing of three young boys.

"You know what might be happening here," Perley said. "He realized his reindeer left evidence in your yard of his scouting out the world before Christmas and came back to get the poop so nobody'd know he'd been here."

"He can have his poop back," the eight-year-old said, handing the sack to Harry Charles.

"No, you keep it," Harry Charles said. "I'm sure he won't mind if you save it until you're older and you can use it as proof that he got caught by surprise by us. You put it up on a shelf and someday it will come in handy if some guy ever says there's no way Santa Claus would ever come to Manyberries."

Christmas Eve that year at the Ranchmen's we were enjoying ouefnog and rum and discussing the magic of the season. It's ouefnog because after Keith Spicer visited and we became bilingual and bicultural, Hazel changed the menus to reflect our French heritage. In other parts of the world they drink eggnog but not here in Manyberries.

Perley came in late, as usual, and said he had been over to say goodnight to his grandsons. It gets dark in the winter long before bedtime and he said the grandsons had their supper early and were in bed long before the last ray of light had faded in the west.

"We've got three true believers over there," he said. "That sack of reindeer poop is on a shelf in their bedroom and all three touched it before we tucked them in. You'd think it was some sort of religious icon the way they looked at it. By the way," he turned to me, "my wife wants her red winter coat back to wear on Boxing Day."

"I still have my sack," Harry Charles said, "except the pellets have all turned to dust, which you'd expect after 70 years, but I still touch it every Christmas Eve before we turn in for the night. You just can't take any chances, especially this close to Christmas morning."

Making Scents in Manyberries

Back in the 1980s there was a move to persuade all hunters to start wearing what they called blaze orange clothing as a safety precaution. Some people called it 40 mile cloth because, it was claimed, you could see it at that distance. It seemed like such a good idea that Purvis, Perley, Harry Charles and I ordered hunting parkas from the Sears catalogue. Up until that time we had all worn dark red and black mackinaw coats and battered red baseball caps, thinking that was sufficient visual evidence to convince other hunters we weren't moose, deer, antelope or ducks.

Our decision to purchase was influenced considerably by a news story about some American hunter shooting two of his hunting partners because he thought they were bears. The two unfortunates had been wearing dark red and black mackinaw coats, along with hats of the same material. Harry Charles remarked that he hoped the shooter discovered his mistake before he started the skinning process.

When the coats arrived, a big argument ensued over whether we'd ever see a deer or any animal within 40 miles because of the blinding orange colour. Harry Charles did some reading somewhere and reported back that animals are either colour-blind or don't bother distinguishing colours. We all wore them into the Ranchmen's to get local reaction and everybody there that night shielded their eyes against the glare. This blaze orange picks up and reflects even the dimmest light. We went out the next evening to some trees about 20 miles distant and took turns walking through them in the dwindling light to see for ourselves. We concluded that even an eastern politician couldn't mistake us for a moose.

When we arrived back at the Ranchmen's, Harry Charles started

And God Created Manyberries

reminiscing about his old Uncle Charlie, one of the best hunters in the Muskoka region of Ontario where Harry Charles was born. "Uncle Charlie," he told us, "would stop washing two weeks before the hunting season and bury all his hunting clothes under cedar boughs in the sawdust pile beside the woodshed. The way he figured it, the deer could detect human scent long before they saw the human and he wanted to rid himself of all human scent, just to get a bit of an edge. I guess Uncle Charlie figured the scent of lye soap would be offensive to deer."

"Hell, the way wind blows out here, an antelope could take a whiff and get the scent of somebody in Lethbridge." Perley likes to keep things simple but I could only guess at the point he was making.

"But I'm talking about deer and if we ever went where there were trees and not as much wind, we'd be at a disadvantage sitting there waiting for a deer to walk by and stinking to the high heavens. And I'm certain a deer would describe human scent as stinking to the high heavens. As Uncle Charlie said, you take whatever edge you can."

"What are you getting at, Harry Charles?" Purvis is always looking for the edge in everything he does, including, we suspect, poker games, where he always insists on supplying the cards, none of which ever come out of a sealed box.

"We should do something with these coats to overpower whatever human scent we carry, like burying them under cedar boughs in a sawdust pile."

"There's no cedar within a couple of hundred miles of here and no sawdust, either," I said. "In fact, the only piles of anything around here can be found alongside corrals and barns and if you think I'm burying my new coat under one of those piles, you are grossly wrong."

Harry Charles pointed down at my boots. "I wasn't suggesting that, but if you are that sensitive, why didn't you scrape your boots before you walked in here?" I looked down at my left boot and saw that I still carried a bit of cow souvenir from our trip out to the trees where we carried out the visual experiment.

"No, I'm suggesting that we find something, a scent, that is distinctly not human and apply it to our coats. It could be anything as long as it couldn't be connected to humans."

"Deer like apples," Purvis said, "maybe we could soak them in apple juice."

"We could spray them with the pine scent stuff my wife leaves in my bathroom," Perley suggested. Perley's house is the only one in Manyberries with two bathrooms and the extra one was built at her insistence.

"Why not just ask our wives if we can use their perfume?" It seemed to me that the wives wouldn't object to that if it would help in our quest for meat for the freezer.

"Do you know how much that stuff costs?" Purvis knows the price of everything and thinks it's too high by at least 50 percent.

"I think perfume is a good idea but we'd have to find some that's cheap and comes in large containers so we can do all four coats," Harry Charles said. He paused and looked at me. "You are going to Calgary, are you not?" I had already said I had to make a quick trip up to Calgary and had volunteered to do any shopping for anybody who needed anything you can't get in Manyberries, which is just about everything. Most times, the Suburban would be loaded down when I returned from Calgary with stuff for nearly everybody in town.

"So maybe you can visit Wal-Mart where they sell stuff in bulk and look around for what we need." Harry Charles pulled a five dollar bill from his wallet. "Here's my five and get a receipt so we can divvy up what's left when you get back." Purvis and Perley dropped two move fives on the table.

"My contribution will be the cost of gasoline there and back," I said. That seemed fair to them. Well, they didn't argue so I assumed it was fair.

It wasn't at Wal-Mart where I found the perfume; it was a Buck or Less store. They had shelves full of tiny little bottles of something called body splash at 99 cents each and I bought 15, generously covering the additional 74 cents for the sales tax.

At the counter I unscrewed the cap on one bottle and took a whiff and my hair stood on end. The girl at the cash asked me to put the cap back quickly. I swear when I left there a cloud of body splash aroma hung in that space like a nuclear mushroom.

Back in Manyberries, we emptied a Windex spray bottle and filled it with body splash and began spraying our coats. We had to move outside Harry Charles' garage for fear of being overcome by the fumes and they ordered me not to light a cigarette until I was at least half way to the Ranchmen's.

The day before deer season opened up north near Drumheller, I picked the three of them up and we sallied forth. They had their hunting clothes stuffed in duffel bags and would change into them in the morning.

It was cold that morning and I went out and started the Suburban and left it running with the heater on so we'd be comfortable on the drive out to where we would hunt deer.

The sneezing and eye-watering started before we'd even gone

two miles. At four miles, Harry Charles leaned over and turned off the heater. At four and a half miles, Purvis and Perley rolled down their windows and the Suburban began to feel like a freezer. At about mile five, Harry Charles rolled down his window and stuck his head out, even though the below-freezing temperature and speed of the Suburban made for a frightful wind-chill factor.

I started to light a cigarette and all three of them yelled at me not to light up for fear we'd be blown all the way back to Manyberries. I took a pinch of Copenhagen instead. They say people used snuff to kill the terrible smells of big cities in Europe before they had sewers and invented motor vehicles to replace the horse-drawn wagons. It didn't work for me.

But something worked on that trip. We got lucky and a deer each and returned to Manyberries three days later. We had learned quickly in Drumheller not to wear our new coats when we went in for a beer and hamburger at night. We did the first night and the waiter took one whiff and back pedalled to the bar and yelled at us he was allergic and couldn't serve us until we got rid of whatever that stink was. We went to the Suburban and removed the coats and returned and were served.

We forgot what we learned in Drumheller and wore our coats into the Ranchmen's on our return.

Hazel got a whiff because of the breeze at our backs when we entered and wondered aloud if somebody had ruptured a sour natural gas line. I didn't think we smelled *that* bad.

Four-Eyed Tom was at our table but moved quickly to one in the corner when we sat down.

Hazel came over with a full tray and retreated, saying there was no way she was going to serve us any more or even tolerate our presence as long as whatever it was we were giving off was being given off.

So, it was out to the Suburban to doff our coats and back in to get a few more visits from Hazel.

She approached hesitantly and took a deep whiff. Satisfied that most of the offending odour had been eliminated she served us. "Even if you got rid of 80 percent of that stink," she said, "some of it lingers. All four of you should take a bath and wash those clothes before you do yourselves any serious damage. And I mean including your long underwear."

That was a lot of years ago, yet still, anytime we are in the Suburban wearing our blaze orange coats with the heater on and windows up, the memory of that hunt remains with us. There could be a song in there: The Maladorous Lingers On.

The Manyberries Boom

"We've just about reached the limit of growth around here," Purvis said, "and if we don't soon, and I mean very soon, develop a management plan for the future, there will be chaos for generations to come."

"What's on your mind, Purvis? The big annual influx doesn't start until six weeks from now." Harry Charles was reading Izaak Walton's treatise on fishing and was leaning back and over to catch the light coming in the heavily curtained front window of the Ranchmen's Saloon. He tucked the book between his thigh and the chair arm and leaned forward. It was now high cocktail time at the Ranchmen's because Purvis had arrived, fresh from either hoeing his turnips or burning out his adding machine calculating his assets, which he does daily.

"I'm not talking about the bird and antelope hunters; I'm talking about a population boom that will put a crushing weight on our infrastructure."

"Somebody expecting a baby?" I asked. "Hadn't heard or seen any evidence of any of the locals planning for a blessed event."

"No, there's a new family moving in: mother, father and three young ones." Perley of course is on top of everything, what with his mail delivering duties and all.

"Yes, and I don't know how we can handle the burden of the demands this will put on our municipal services. Thank you, Hazel." Purvis made a scribbling gesture with his right hand on his upturned left palm to indicate he'd pay later, which he always does and which he has always done. It's one of his habits that either endears him to you or irritates the hell out of you because he's been doing it for 20 years.

"We actually don't have much in the way of municipal services,

And God Created Manyberries

Purvis," Harry Charles said, "unless you count Perley's mail service, or the Alberta Highways guys who drive by every once in a while."

"Don't forget that we get the telephone line guys stopping in from time to time to look up at the wires," Perley added.

"I don't mean just those services, I mean the other stuff, like sewers and stringing wire to where they're going to build so they can have lights and a telephone. When you start building out from the inner core without having a plan, you've got the potential for ugly urban sprawl."

"You mean like they have in Calgary and Edmonton or Toronto?" Harry Charles figures Calgary and Edmonton are trying hard to be like Toronto while Toronto is trying hard to be like an American city, preferably New York but failing that, Buffalo, New York, a city with standards that Toronto on a good day can almost measure up to.

"Precisely, and look at what they're experiencing: long time residents facing traffic congestion at all hours, tiny scrunched-up lots with massive houses, miles and miles of Tim Hortons joints on every corner, higher and higher taxes to pay for the services those newcomers are demanding. There's no telling where it will end and all because nobody ever had a plan. We can't let that happen here." You could tell that Purvis was very exercised because the vein on his forehead had swollen and he neglected to wipe the beer foam from his upper lip.

"Well, I can hardly think that five more people will put an unbearable strain on us here in Manyberries," Harry Charles said. Five more would be, umm, only five percent added to our population. We're still at 100, aren't we, Perley?"

"Actually, the last count was 101 and nobody on my mail route has died, but 100 is close enough, at least until young Crawford's wife delivers and my wife says she's big enough to be carrying twins."

Purvis could see that his concern wasn't going to be shared by any of the others at that table. Four-Eyed Tom was working on one of his crossword puzzles and didn't appear to be engaged in the debate.

"But look at it this way," Purvis argued. "If we get five percent this year and five percent next year and so on like that for 10 years, we would be close to doubling the population. What are you going to do with a population of 200 people when you've lived with a population of 100 all these years?"

"Well, it'd probably keep the Ranchmen's from going under and maybe we'd even get a Tim Hortons. I like their doughnuts." I was wrong – Four-Eyed Tom was engaged.

"Geez, if we get a Tim Hortons, I think I'll move to the country," Harry Charles said. "Maybe over to Onefour, because hardly anybody lives there now and I can't recall meeting anyone who expressed any interest."

Onefour is even smaller than Manyberries and is so named because a long time ago it was 14 miles from somewhere else. It doesn't have a saloon.

"Yeah, if Tim Hortons moved in, it's a sure bet that McDonald's would be on their heels and after that who knows, maybe one of those pizza joints," Perley paused. "Well, maybe a small pizza place, if they deliver. When we visit the daughter up in Calgary, they always order pizza on Fridays and a man could get addicted to that. I like the ones with extra hot pepperoni, although I always regret it the next morning."

"Well, all I can say is you wait and see," Purvis said huffily. "Uncontrolled growth, municipal services stretched to the limit, sky-high property taxes, that's what's in store if we allow this to happen without a plan. Look at Calgary and you'll see what I mean. Look at Alberta for that matter. It's a mess because nobody had a plan." Purvis signalled to Hazel by making a scribbling gesture with his right hand on his upturned left palm to indicate that he was leaving but would return later for more and to pay his bill.

When he was gone, Harry Charles turned to Perley. "That was out of character for Purvis. He's always Johnny-on-the-spot when there might be a chance to make a buck and with newcomers, there's always that chance."

"Yeah, well, that's what's eating him this time. The newcomers bought that extra lot Old Rutherford and the Mrs own back of their garden."

"That's a nice lot," I said. "Looks to be about 100 feet deep and 75 wide. Wonder what they paid Old Rutherford?"

"Four thousand, three hundred dollars and it has the hydro line only two poles away. Old Rutherford got more for that than he paid for all the lots he owns, if he ever sub-divided the rest of it."

"Well, good for Old Rutherford, I say," said Harry Charles. "The old boy and the Mrs can probably buy themselves twin sunlamps for the winter."

"Well, that's really what's rankling Purvis," Perley said. "Old Rutherford got the sale and they didn't even look at any of the lots Purvis owns. Mrs. Purvis told me he was prepared to sell any of his for a flat $5000 but nobody knew he wanted to sell."

"I wonder where he went and what he's up to? Knowing Purvis he's probably got some plan or scheme to make at least as much as Old Rutherford."

"He's over visiting Thor. She's taking calligraphy correspondence courses and he's paying her to draw some For Sale signs."

Over-Exposed in Manyberries

Perley walked into the Ranchmen's late one afternoon with a week-old copy of the Edmonton Sun and asked if we had heard of the man in Kingston, Ontario who spoiled the appetites of a bunch of restaurant diners.

Usually we get old copies of the Calgary Sun for our daily read and delivery of the Edmonton version meant that somebody from the far north was visiting.

"Nope, that's a new one to me," Harry Charles responded. "But then, most times if I see the story is about places like Kingston, Ontario, I skip them no matter what the headline says. Not that there's anything wrong with Kingston but it's sort of like Toronto – nothing ever happens there."

"Well, it's what you'd expect in a big city like Kingston," Perley said and dropped the newspaper in the puddles on the table. "It's scandalous and outrageous, and to think that I got off the train there on my way to the war. You wouldn't have seen behaviour like that in those days."

I picked up the newspaper to read the offending story. Apparently some man had decided to entertain the patrons of the restaurant by doing an impromptu dance on the sidewalk and during his shuffle had exposed himself. Perhaps energized and inspired by the expressions on the faces of those at the tables inside, he shuffled right up to the bay window and smooshed his penis against the glass.

As I was reading the story Perley was giving Harry Charles a verbal summary.

"I was wrong and I apologize to Kingston," Harry Charles said. "Sometimes things do happen there."

"Well, I don't find it all that shocking," I said. "Not that long ago,

Old Rutherford and the Mrs were cleaning their windows and in their usual state of nudity. You should have seen what was pressed up against their windows."

"That's irrelevant," Perley said. "You weren't sitting at a table enjoying a meal with a companion, you were outside walking by and looking in. It would be different if you were sitting on a patio eating a pizza and they did that from the inside looking out to shock or titillate you."

"I don't think that shock or titillation would be my reaction," Harry Charles said. "And I'm not going to give myself a brain hernia trying to visualize Old Rutherford and the Mrs pressing the glass, if that's an apt expression."

"Well, I'd be deeply offended if I was sitting there with the wife eating a pizza and that happened," Perley huffed. "It'd probably put both of us off our appetites."

"It would be a lot worse if you had been sitting there eating spotted dick or bratwurst and sauerkraut," Harry Charles observed.

And that's when Perley and I nearly fell off our chairs laughing.

A New School for Manyberries

Purvis came in huffing and puffing as if he had walked the whole several hundred yards from his house to the Ranchmen's. He had a magazine supplement from the Calgary Herald in his hand and looked like somebody who had just won the lottery.

As it turned out, he had walked because he was in such a hurry he didn't want to waste time looking for the keys to his pickup.

"Here it is, boys, the future of Manyberries," and he plunked the magazine down in the middle of the table. "Somebody dropped this on my front porch and it's a, umm, what they call, you know, one of those things that lets you see into the future. An ominum."

"Or an omen," Harry Charles said.

"Yeah, that's the word. Read this and you'll see what I mean." Nobody picked it up because we've learned not to get too excited when Purvis does because you never know what might happen.

"They've got a hockey school in Warner for girls and they're bringing them in from all over the country," he said, "and it's just that sort of thinking we need here in Manyberries. If we want to thrive and prosper, that is."

"Why would we want to build a hockey rink for girls when Warner already has one?" Perley wondered. "And besides, how many girls are there who want to play hockey? And besides the besides, how many people want to go and watch girls play hockey?"

"I don't mean we should build a school for girl hockey. I mean we should put our thinking caps on and come up with a school idea that would have the parents of rich kids from Toronto, Calgary or even Medicine Hat scrambling to get their kids in on it."

"Well, we do have the Horsepersonship lessons at the school," I suggested. In fact, it's called Horsemanship but I lived for a time in Ottawa and haven't yet scraped all of that off my brain.

"No, that's for the locals, part of our history and culture. I'm talking about something new and exciting that will drag in crowds of young people with all that new money their parents are itching to burn."

"You could be on to something here, Purvis," Harry Charles leaned forward in his pretend excited way. "You know, they even featured the Warner Hockey School when they had that Hockey Day in Canada thing."

"That's in this story too, that Warner got featured on national television. I tell you guys, if we can come up with an idea here there's no end to the attention we'll get and the money we can generate."

"Well, what sports do we have besides hockey that we can consider?" Perley held up his hand to indicate he had his own answers. "There's baseball with either the big or small balls. There's soccer, football, rugby, basketball, golf, badminton, tennis, hunting, fishing and, well, a lot of choices. The question is, which sport would draw the attention of parents with loads of money to spend?"

"Scratch out hunting and fishing," Harry Charles said. "There's no way I'm taking anybody to any of my favourite spots."

"Golf is out of the question," I said, "unless we invest a few million in a golf course. Or train the dogs to fetch golf balls out on the prairie."

"Well, golf is a stupid game anyway," Harry Charles said, "ranking down there with skiing. You hit a ball and chase after it or get a lift up a hill only to come right back down again and then do it all over." Harry Charles knows I've spent a lifetime trying to justify calling myself a golfer. He also knows I wrecked myself the last time I skied.

"I forgot to mention skiing," Perley said. "But we could never raise the money it would take to build a mountain anyway."

"What about tennis?" Purvis wondered. "Don't all the rich people play tennis?"

"I think you're getting close," Harry Charles said. "Not that I'd stand up here at the window to watch a tennis game, but they do draw big crowds at those tournaments."

"So what do we need to get started? Some paved ground and white paint." Purvis paused. "Hell, I've got gallons of white paint in my shed and to get started we could bring in a tractor to level the ground over near the community centre."

"But how would we flatten and pave it?" Perley must have watched tennis on television one time because his question indicated some knowledge of the game.

"Oil drums. Forty-five gallon oil drums filled with sand. After the tractor gets done, we drag these oil drums full of sand back and forth until it's hard and smooth. Then later, when the revenues start rolling in, we hire a road contractor to come in and lay down asphalt."

"Purvis, you're a man ahead of his time," Harry Charles said. "Tennis is a coed game and while Warner has only girls, Manyberries could have both boy and girl students at our tennis school. That means double the potential revenues and profits." Harry Charles lifted a hand in the air to signal Hazel that we needed some serious refills to fuel a serious conversation.

"Geez, I never thought of that," Purvis said. "But you're right, when I get a vision there's no telling where it'll end."

"What about accommodation" Perley asked. "If we get a few hundred boys and girls here, they'll have to have some place to sleep. Not to forget eat."

"The community hall. We could set it up as a dormitory. We could get bunk beds, some bed reading lamps, whatever it takes."

"You're planning on having teenage boys and girls all sleeping in the same hall?" Harry Charles shook his head.

"Okay, so buy some curtains to hang between the boys and girls sections so they'd have some privacy."

"You're only going to have curtains hanging between hormone-raging boys and girls, some of them perhaps not even beyond the age of legal consent?" Harry Charles shook his head again. "I don't think even tennis parents are going to be on board with that, Purvis."

"Okay, so we start with boys or girls only and when we get rolling, and can afford it, we build another hall for whatever sex we didn't start with first."

"What about shower and toilet facilities?" Perley wondered. "That's a lot of plumbing."

"The community hall has two outhouses. We could use some of my white paint to give them a freshening and we could build some shower stalls and run a hose over from the closest house."

"Showering under a garden hose – man, I just can't wait to hear the screams when some kid stands under that some cold and frosty morning." Harry Charles shook his head again.

"All you're doing, Harry Charles, is looking at the negatives. Those are details that shouldn't stand in the way of our vision."

"Your vision, Purvis. You thought of it and you should take all the credit for it." Harry Charles has always been very generous with giving Purvis the credit for his initiatives. The rest of us are the same because more often than not, Purvis's initiatives get more blame than credit.

"Okay, so we've got some details to consider. What's a fair estimate of how much it would take to get a school set up with a dormitory, showers and toilets, paved courts with nets, a dining hall with kitchen, equipment, advertising and teachers? A couple of thousand bucks? Remember, I've got lots of paint."

Harry Charles took out his little spiral shirt pocket notebook and ballpoint and began writing out figures. When he finished, he looked up and shook his head. "I'd say at minimum, and I stress minimum, we're looking at between a half and a full million dollars."

Purvis swallowed hard and got flushed. "Geez, where in hell did Warner ever come up with that kind of money? There's not even 400 people living there and they don't get any more money from the government than we do."

"Well, they do have the infrastructure since they already had an indoor rink. But don't let the costs deter you, Purvis." Harry Charles wasn't going to let Purvis let his dream expire. "Think about some other sport, one that doesn't require that much start-up cash. You need to come up with something that would appeal to parents who want their kids to learn and excel at and that would get the kids excited as well."

Purvis turned to Perley. "When you ran down that list of sports, did you mention poker?"

"No, but there's nobody stopping you if decide to declare poker is a sport and open a school where it can be learned."

"Okay, I'm going to think about it and tell you what I decide tomorrow. I've gotta go now."

"Where in hell did Purvis get this from?" Perley picked up the Calgary Herald supplement and waved it at Hazel to indicate those of us who remained would like a little refill attention.

"I slipped over and dropped it on his porch early this morning," Harry Charles said. "Opened at the story about Warner's hockey school for girls."

"You know, Harry Charles, one of these days you're going to plant a seed in Purvis and, if it ever germinates, it's going to blow Manyberries right off the map."

Eddie Conquers Manyberries

Jennifer brought Eddie to visit a few weekends ago and the town is still in turmoil talking about it.

Jennifer is my daughter and Eddie is a Jack Russell terrier. People who know dogs say they should be called Jack Russell Terrorists.

I don't know about other Jack Russells but Eddie walks tall. He doesn't stand much more than a foot above the ground at the shoulders even in winter when he's wearing his leather booties. He hates his leather booties because, I suspect, he thinks they're for sissies. But he's realistic enough to recognize that at 30 below with a howling wind only a fool would mind looking a little sissified.

You should know that Jack Russells apparently came along as a breed after the English Protestants and Catholics stopped killing each other. I guess they got tired of that because it was some sort of cleric named Jack Russell who wanted a type of dog that would kill other animals, especially badgers and rats. I've never wanted to visit England in case there's something in the water that makes the English that way.

Eddie by the way should in no way be confused with Eddie the hairy Jack Russell on that television show. Our Eddie is a smooth hair J.R. and would never sit still and look quizzically as people knocked at the front door. Eddie shares a trait that all the dogs in our family have had. When somebody knocks at the front door they go at that door in a barking frenzy and at such speed that they can't stop and often find themselves walking about on wobbly legs after suffering a near concussion.

Anyway, Eddie came on down from Calgary and it was his first visit and he set about acquainting himself with the yard and every fence post and picket surrounding it and every shrub we had planted.

He was probably on his last shrub when he spotted the town jackrabbit. This jackrabbit is a little bit strange. He lives a solitary existence under a trailer on the outskirts of town and takes a daily stroll pausing only to nibble a little greenery here and there. Nobody ever bothers him and I don't think anybody's so much as taken a shot at him and that's strange because jackrabbits are generally seen as fair game. Even the dogs have taken to ignoring him because they've never been able to catch him and why waste your time and energy in hot pursuit if there's no hot lunch at the end of it?

Well, Eddie spotted him and he did what I call the Eddie Stand Tall. It seems Eddie's got the idea if you stand tall you are tall. It's my own non-scientific opinion that when Eddie does his stand tall routine, in his mind he is instantly somewhere around 10 feet tall and, it should be added, bullet-proof. Whenever he sees what might be an enemy, Eddie automatically does his stand tall routine. Possible enemies include all dogs, all cats except TLC, people who walk by on the front sidewalk when he's looking out the window, service station people who still come out to your pickup and put the gasoline in for you, people at drive-through windows at hamburger joints, and anybody walking through a parking lot when Eddie's alone in the car. There are others but they're too numerous to mention.

So Eddie did his split second stand tall routine and then sailed over that 16 inch high picket fence like it was only 16 inches high and made a beeline for that rabbit.

Jackrabbits are prairie animals and the species hasn't survived because of poor eyesight. This one saw Eddie coming before his feet hit the ground and got into a comfortable lope, heading back to his trailer. I don't know if the rabbit had it timed or if it was coincidence but as he rounded the corner, Perley was headed down his walk to the gate.

Eddie was almost within grabbing distance when the jackrabbit gave a little jump ahead just as Perley swung open his gate. Eddie didn't stand a chance and nor did Perley's left shin. Eddie's head slammed into the gate with such force that the gate swung back and the lower cross piece caught Perley in the shin just above ankle bone level.

The pain of a sharp rap on the shin bone is enough to make grown men cry and Perley was always a little emotional anyway. Eddie was lying on his side wondering if all jackrabbits kicked as hard as mules. It took a bit of time for the two of them to recover. The jackrabbit went on back to his trailer.

Eddie was pretty subdued for the rest of the day and Perley got a lot of sympathy on his rounds and a few extra beers when he limped into the Ranchmen's Saloon.

　　　　　　　　　　　And God Created Manyberries

On Sunday, we decided to go for a stroll before the town started to stir. You generally have until noon for such strolls because nobody stirs much, except the dogs, until noon.

It was just Eddie and me and we were trying to decide whether to walk around block one or block two, there being only two blocks in town, when the Purvis dog, Three-Eyed Tom, ambled out on the street looking for a vehicle on which to relieve himself. Eddie went into his Stand Tall and You Are Tall routine.

Three-Eyed Tom, the biggest and toughest dog anybody ever saw, only glanced at Eddie and gave a dismissive growl. No dog ever challenged Three-Eyed Tom. This is one big dog and is probably a mix of all the big breed dogs in the world. You don't want to be in a low-slung convertible sports car if Three-Eyed Tom is looking to relieve himself on a vehicle. Not with the top and windows down.

He's called Three-Eyed because just above and right between his eyes he has a white spot on an otherwise black head. Somebody threw in Tom for unknown reasons.

You have to know something else as well about Manyberries and that is there are a lot of dogs in town. Most of them are male dogs that haven't been "altered" and because of that they are territorial. Manyberries dogs don't much care for each other but they hate strange dogs. I don't know about the bitches, if there are any, and their likes and dislikes. Hazel down at the Ranchmen's Saloon will pause between wiping up puddles of beer on the bar and tell you that Manyberries has more dogs per capita than any town in the world. "And we have our share of bitches too," she'll say. Everybody knows what she means but nobody's brave enough to ask her who she means.

Eddie went after Three-Eyed and it was my fault because I neglected to leash him when we left the house. The big dog turned to stare Eddie down but that's like trying to exhale a tornado into reverse.

Eddie did one more Stand Tall and You Are Tall routine and returned the stare. Actually, Eddie was probably staring between his legs at about knee-level and seeing the prairie out past where the railroad used to be.

It was Three-Eyed who moved first and he feinted left. Eddie was quicker and he went at his enemy on his right flank. By the time Three-Eyed recovered Eddie was on him. Not exactly on him but under him.

Eddie could have bitten Three-Eyed Tom on a hind leg but he went for something better. He reached up and grabbed Three-Eyed Tom on that part of the anatomy where it is generally accepted the majority of males of all species store their brains.

It happened fast but I am convinced to this day that all three of Three-Eyed Tom's eyes bugged out of his head when he realized that Eddie had him locked in a death grip. He started to run and he was making puppy-like yelps of surrender but Eddie was tenacious.

I don't think Three-Eyed Tom travelled more than 10 or 12 inches but any fool could see he was beaten and surrendering so Eddie let him go.

We continued our stroll without interruption and never encountered another dog. It was decided some days later at the Ranchmen's that maybe there's some sort of dogs-only communications network that gets word around fast because not one dog came to the fence to peer through the pickets and growl and not one jumped a fence to challenge Eddie. Not in all the history of Manyberries has a strange dog strolled around town without a challenge.

When we got back to the house, no amount of coaxing could get Eddie inside. He parked himself at the gate and guarded that yard and house as tenaciously as he had held on to Three-Eyed Tom. I even think he was reluctant to get into the car to head back to Calgary. Why would anybody want to leave a town they own?

I can tell you that after Three-Eyed Tom sailed over the fence into the sanctuary of his yard and Eddie came trotting back to me I swear that he was actually close to 14 feet tall right up until he got alongside me and looked up and I had to bend over to rub his ears.

Entitlement –
A Canadian Obsession

"So you've been away?" Perley asked, as I walked in shortly after my return from a month in Palm Springs. "Somebody wondered where you were after he found a copy of the Calgary Herald with your name in it. He said you agree with two of the Premiers on the east coast about how they should get more money from offshore oil."

"Yeah, before I left I wrote a letter to the editor saying I had a similar grievance."

"Well, it got passed around and a lot of the guys who read it were wondering if maybe it was time you moved back to Ottawa."

"Did you read it?" I asked. "Did Purvis and Harry Charles read it?"

"Yes, I did and they did, as did Four-Eyed Tom. It took a while for Purvis and Four-Eyed to settle down. They both think Danny Williams and Rodney MacDonald are part of the greedy, grasping Premiers' crowd who won't accept a good thing when it's handed to them. They think that if you're siding with them then maybe you'd be happier back in Ottawa."

"What did you think"?

"Well, Harry Charles and I got a chuckle out of it and decided rather than get into it, we'd wait until you dropped in and you could defend yourself. We thought there'd be at least a week of entertainment here while you explained the concept of sarcasm and irony."

"You don't mean to tell me that I'm going to have to spend the next dozen cocktail hours parsing that letter for people and explaining what I really meant? Geez, if I could afford it, I'd head back to Palm Springs until they forget about it."

Reader says if Danny's entitled, so is he

Friday, April 06, 2007

Re: "N.S. Threatens to sue Ottawa in fight over offshore deal,"
  March 25

Like Atlantic premiers Rodney MacDonald and Danny Williams, I have a grievance.

When I was a young man, my father gave me a generous allowance every week which gave me the freedom to see movies, secretly buy cigarettes and occasionally have a surplus before the next week's allowance was delivered. But then, without warning, my father withdrew the allowance when I reached my mid-20s and was working full time. He even withdrew the supplementary amounts I had come to depend on to buy gas for my car, pay the insurance on it, and part of the rent for my apartment. I am considering following Nova Scotia and Newfoundland's lead and suing my long-departed father, using the generous inheritance he left me to cover the legal costs.

It's time we Canadians stood up for our entitlements.

There was a photo of Danny Williams accompanying the letter with the caption "Reader figures he can take a leaf out of Newfoundland Premier Danny Williams' book."

"I can't figure out how anyone, except maybe Danny Williams and Rodney MacDonald, would have read that and interpreted it as support for them."

"Harry Charles said he wouldn't be surprised if Williams and MacDonald took that and framed it to hang in their offices to show there's agreement with their cause even in Alberta. He says he won't be surprised if Ed Stelmach holds it up as evidence that Albertans believe we should either get more from Ottawa or send less down there."

"So what was the point of the discussion around here after they read it?"

"Nobody thinks Williams and MacDonald have a leg to stand on and are professional whiners. But most would agree with Stelmach that we should send less to Ottawa so he would have more to give to us. After all, we are entitled to our fair share and right now, that's not enough for most folks."

"So you could say I struck a chord?"

"Oh, you struck a chord alright. There was talk that night that maybe it was time to overhaul the Constitution so that Manyberries

And God Created Manyberries

stops supporting the Atlantic Provinces. As Purvis said, we could use that money to grow our pie. He still quotes Belinda from time to time."

"Well, it's not often a letter to the editor sparks such heated debate so I can take some small comfort from that."

"Harry Charles had a good suggestion. He said it has been nearly six months since somebody organized a new political party so it's time for another. He suggested we need a Me First party and you should lead it. He said the way voters think, you could bounce Stelmach out of office and wind up as Premier. Then you expand and lead the charge into Ottawa."

"But only if they take everything I say and promise literally, right?"

"Yeah, but why should that be a concern? After all, we are Canadians."

Get The Puck Outta There

"How many idiots are there in Parliament?" Harry Charles asked me when I settled into my chair for the cocktail hour.

"How many angels can dance on a pin? Why do you ask?"

"Have you read about this kerfuffle over Shane Doan and how those idiots are holding Parliamentary Committee hearings into something that was settled two years ago?"

"Yeah, there was something this morning on the news about it." I shook my head, as much in embarrassment as bewilderment, and waved hello at Hazel to let her know she could begin the first of many treks from the bar to our table.

Shane Doan, a very pleasant young man and a great hockey player, had been accused of making a slur against referees during a game, allegedly referring to their Quebecois roots or loyalties, or at least that's what I gathered from the radio report. Officials of the NHL had investigated and cleared him.

Harry Charles had a black notebook opened on the table and a ballpoint in hand.

"What are you writing?"

"I'm preparing my political analysis column for the next edition of the Bald Prairie Tattler."

"That's not due out for another eight months so why the rush?"

"I'll be touching on several subjects and one will be the shameless way the media have handled this Shane Doan affair. I want to get it down now while my outrage is still fresh in my mind."

"What's the thrust of your piece, if you don't mind scooping yourself eight months in advance?"

"I'm thinking the Bloc Quebecois, New Democrats, Liberals and probably even the Green Party, if they had been there, are guilty of shameless pandering to the Quebec media."

And God Created Manyberries

"So you're giving the Conservatives a pass on this one? They let it come before the Parliamentary Committee, so don't they deserve a slap too?"

"No, I think they saw what I'd call a McCarthy opportunity and seized it. Do you remember the McCarthy hearings in the U.S. back in the 50s?"

"I read about them. Can't remember the details except that McCarthy wound up looking brutish and stupid and blew himself out of the water."

"Exactly. The Bloc Quebecois, New Democrats, Liberals, Gilles Duceppe, Jack Layton and Stéphane Dion all look brutish and stupid, and ordinary people in Quebec and all over Canada probably believe that. And if they don't my column will tell them they should."

"Well, I don't want to throw water on your outrage but that might be a little convoluted for the average reader. Not to suggest that your readers are only average."

"I thought of that, but I have to write something to justify the headline and it's just too good a line to throw away. You want to hear the headline?"

"Harry Charles, why do you ask when we both know you're going to tell me?"

"I'm making it all upper case: GET THE PUCK OUTTA THERE."

"That's a great headline. But I think you should go tabloid with the body of the story too rather than delve into McCarthy and the witch-hunt and Edward R. Murrow so you'll still have space for what's really important to readers."

"Yeah, I do have another subject that's too good to drop. How about if I use the headline and then in my analysis make a very succinct comment? I think maybe I could just write 'As far as the Shane Doan affair of recent months on Parliament Hill is concerned, it is your correspondent's carefully considered opinion that the Bloc Quebecois, New Democrats and Liberals should have kept the puck out of there.'"

I tipped my wine glass to toast his editorial acumen and put a hand up for Hazel to see.

"You said you have another subject for the column? Is it about hunting or fishing, which is, after all, the purpose of the newsletter?"

"Yeah, this is a good one. It's about Canada Post writing to some guy in Winnipeg to tell him they were no longer going to deliver mail to his house because his cat hides under the porch and growls when the mailman comes."

"You're kidding me. That's gotta be one of those urban myths."

"No, it's right here in this clipping from the Calgary Sun," and he waved it in the air. "It says a reporter went to the guy's house and when he approached the cat, it rolled over on his back so its belly could be scratched. The cat's human was trying to make a point about how friendly the cat is."

"What does this have to do with hunting and fishing?"

"I was thinking about writing how the mailman and his supervisors and whoever runs Canada Post in Ottawa should be hunted down and fired for ineptitude and stupidity. I bet Perley would agree to tack his by-line on it, too. " He thanked Hazel for the glass she put down and took a swallow. "By the way, I might have some space in my column for a guest comment. Would you like to explain why the Ottawa media write about crap like the Shane Doan affair when there's so much more important stuff happening, like this cat story?"

"No thanks. I've been asking that question as far back as '64 when I first went to Ottawa and was part of it. I still don't have an answer."

Hank and The Catnurse

Weimaraners are not a familiar breed of dog to most people. But those who've known them, or who've been owned by them, are a lot like the people who make the annual pilgrimage to Graceland to remember Elvis – a little demented in their devotion.

Hank was the third "Weim", as they are affectionately called by their crazed fans, to grace our lives with his presence. Like others of his breed, he was willing, most of the time, to adapt his schedule to ours. In the morning, if you slept past 5:00, he'd wait patiently for sometimes as much as three minutes before jumping on the bed to let you know he wanted the back door opened. If his water bowl needed freshening, he'd signal you by putting his nose under the toilet lid and lifting it just far enough to make a noise when it slammed back down. And he'd do that for as long as it took to get somebody's attention.

He was a great companion in the field or around the house. He was always happy to go out hunting with me even for several nights away from his antique chaise and he'd hunt as hard as I would, although to be honest, I don't hunt very hard. The way I have it figured is there is no point wearing yourself out in one hunting season because a new one comes along every autumn. Hank had pretty much the same philosophy – treat this as a stroll in the sunshine and don't let achievement or success be an aggravating motivator. Your nerves can get all jangly if all you seek is success. The last thing any Weimaraner wants to be is jangly and that's pretty good advice for humans too.

One thing Hank liked when we were hunting was deep-fried duck breast. We'd shoot a couple of ducks and fire up Harry Charles' antique white gas camp stove and fry the breasts in extra virgin olive oil along with some potatoes and whatever else was in the grub box. Hank always got one single breast and a piece of potato. It was Harry Charles' belief that if you shared the bounty of the hunt with your hunting companions, they'd be more eager to hunt the next time. I don't know about Hank but it sure worked for Harry Charles, Perley and me.

If we were camping out in the Suburban, Hank generously shared his company equally with us. I'd sleep on the front seat where I could reach the ignition key and turn the motor on to get a little heat every hour or so. Harry Charles and Perley would be in the back in eiderdown sleeping bags. Hank would curl up with them for an hour so and then climb over the back seat and try to get on the front seat with me. He would step on me on his way down to the floor to be close to the heater fan and stay there until I switched the engine off, at which point he'd make his return journey to nest with the guys in the back. It was worse in motels because he would try to leap from bed to bed and often missed and wound up sprawled on the floor.

But it was at home where Hank really shone. We had two cats, Indy and Spook, plus Charlie, who was never quite sure if he was all dog, or half-cat and half-dog or maybe some species as yet undiscovered. All four got along famously but it was Indy who took a shine to Hank and kind of adopted him.

Indy was a very nervous cat who'd run and hide when the doorbell chimed or somebody knocked on the back door. Charlie and Hank would go leaping over one another, barking at the top of their lungs and bang headfirst into the door or anybody who happened to get in their way. Hours after the visitor departed, Indy would reappear and take up position within inches of Hank.

It was strange to see these two. Indy would groom Hank as if he were one of her kittens and he'd stretch out and let her lick his ears or head and if he could have purred like a kitten he would have.

Hank's bed in my office was an antique chaise lounge wingchair that he could settle back into comfortably between the arms, curled up tight and warm. Indy would sleep as close to him as was safe. Dogs do get up in the night and change positions and at 80 pounds if Hank had stepped on her, well, it probably wouldn't have been pretty.

Hank went off sometimes to dog shows where he terrorized the other dogs and sometimes came back with a ribbon or two and Indy would be very restless while he was gone. I'm sure she was restless when Hank went hunting with us, but because I was gone too, I can't testify to her restlessness during those times.

And God Created Manyberries

She stuck like a burr to him when he was at home and we decided she had adopted him as her protector and in turn gave him a lot of mothering. She'd still streak for safety when visitors came and Hank and Charlie put up their howls of welcome but when things were quiet, she'd be there right beside Hank, night and day.

In his later years Hank developed diabetes and then cataracts. His hunting days were pretty much over by then and he had earned a comfortable retirement so about all he had to do was pad around until he found where the sun was shining through a window and settle down with a sigh. Indy would be right beside him and follow him wherever he went, even if he went outside to visit his favourite tree.

As time went on, the cataracts got worse and Hank eventually went blind. He could still find his way around the house because he knew where every chair, sofa and lamp was and not once did he ever knock anything over. As he walked around the house, slowly, Indy would walk ahead of him.

He still went to sleep in that antique chaise every night and Indy would be there beside him, still grooming him with her tongue whenever the notion took her.

One night, I was in the office when Hank decided it was time for bed and he walked in with Indy leading the way.

He got a whiff of me and came over to get his ears scratched while Indy went and jumped up on his bed. I obliged with some ear rubs and then he turned back toward the chaise. He was a few steps away from the chaise and Indy was leaning out and swiping at him with her paw. He inched a little closer and she was able to pat his nose. He then moved confidently forward until he bumped chest first into the chaise and climbed up on it. He got comfortable and settled and Indy settled down beside him.

The next night I followed them when they went to the office. Indy was leading the way with Hank following close behind.

It was the same routine as the night before. Indy was leading him and he was following her scent. She jumped up on the chaise and reached out and tapped him on the nose with her paw. He could then judge how far he was from bumping into the chaise. After that it was easy for a big dog like Hank to get his forepaws up on it and give a little push with his hind legs to get fully up on it. He curled up and Indy curled up beside him.

I watched after that and saw that Indy had become Hank's nurse and guide cat. If he was heading for the back door to visit his tree, she'd be there ahead of him and would wait until he was done visiting and lead him back to the deck and across it to the door.

That went on for a few years and then one night I heard Hank making strange sounds and went into the office and saw that he was dying. I held on to him so he'd know he wasn't alone and Indy sat and stared. When he was gone, I carried him out to the garage but Indy stayed in the office.

After Hank left and Indy had searched the house a few times, she started to lose her appetite and then her fur. She hung on for a few more years but I think when she lost her patient she sort of lost her purpose in life.

When I told Harry Charles about the way Indy nursed Hank he got misty-eyed and said humans could learn a lot by observing animals. He said if they really paid attention, some people might even learn how to be real human.

Elizabeth! May Day! May Day!

"Did you hear what Elizabeth May said about Stephen Harper and the Conservatives last weekend?" Harry Charles asked as he settled into his chair for the cocktail hour.

"Who's Elizabeth May?" Purvis asked.

"She's the leader of the Green Party," Perley explained. "That's the bunch that wants to confiscate your pickup so you can't drive over here from your house every day. Except Sunday, when you stay home or visit the grandchildren."

"What's the Green Party?" Purvis wondered and waved at Hazel to let her know the proceedings on his side of the table could begin.

"It's an environmental rights party and if she gets elected, she'll probably join the Liberals in some sort of unholy political matrimony. She's already halfway there."

Harry Charles and I waited patiently while Purvis received his political science briefing from Perley. It's not that Purvis doesn't keep himself up to speed on politics. He follows avidly reports on what or whom Belinda Stronach is wearing or dating and sometimes thinking, and votes Conservative at all three levels of government. He believes, or hopes, Belinda will return to her senses and rejoin the Conservatives. Harry Charles says even God can't go back to where She's never been.

"What do you mean halfway there? If this Elizabeth May or whoever is leading a party, how can she be halfway to being a Liberal?"

"Stéphane Dion says he won't allow a Liberal to run in the riding she's chosen for the next election, which happens to be Peter

MacKay's riding down in Nova Scotia."

"You mean somebody nobody's ever heard about who's leading a party nobody knows about thinks she can knock off Peter?"

"Yep, that's it in a nutshell and now you're up to speed," Perley said, turning to Harry Charles. "So what did she say?"

"She likened the Conservative policy on the environment to Neville Chamberlain's appeasement of the Nazis."

Purvis thanked Hazel for the mugs and took a grateful swallow. "Who's Neville Chamberlain?"

"Nobody you'd know or want to know," Harry Charles said. "But it sounds as if her new status has caused something to go to, or out of, her head."

"I don't understand what the environment has to do with the Nazis." Purvis shook his head and put some more down the hatch.

"I guess if there was a point to all of this that would be it," Harry Charles said, shaking his head and turning to me. "Didn't you once tell me that Ernst Zundel ran for the leadership of the Liberal Party?"

"Yeah, back in '68, but for some reason they opted for Pierre Trudeau. I still have a copy of Zundel's speech somewhere in my files. I'd have to check to be certain but I don't think he made any mention of the environment."

"Somebody in the media should have reminded Elizabeth May of that, or mentioned in the story that the party she's running for while running for her own party once had Zundel as a leadership candidate."

It was at this point that Purvis excused himself and wandered over to interrupt Four-Eyed Tom in the corner where he works on his crossword puzzles.

"Purvis gets restless when the politics get too scientific," Perley explained and waved at Hazel to reload the table.

"You know," I told them, "a couple of times when I thought it was appropriate or advantageous I did tell several media people that Zundel had once run for the Liberal leadership. One of them called me a bald-faced liar and the rest just laughed. It was like trying to sell meat to a vegetarian, which for all I know maybe they all were. Anyway, when they were accusing Reform of harbouring all sorts of rabid right-wingers, neo-Nazis, bigots and anti-immigrants, they weren't going to waste space admitting that all parties attract their fair share of those types."

Purvis returned from Four-Eyed Tom's table and settled back into his chair. "Who's Ernst Zundel?"

"No friend of Neville Chamberlain," Harry Charles said. "Why do

And God Created Manyberries

you think the media forget that Zundel ran for the Liberals?"

"They didn't forget – they never knew. I believe most of them weren't even born back then."

"Did you guys hear that Belinda is raising money to buy mosquito nets for kids in Africa?" Purvis asked, returning the discussion to a topic he found more interesting. "They'll put them over their beds so the mosquitoes can't get at them while they're sleeping. I was thinking of cutting a cheque and sending it to her with a little personal note."

"That's very generous of you, Purvis," Perley told him. "What would you say to her in the note?"

"I'd congratulate her for what she's doing to help the poor kids and ask her for information on those African mosquitoes because that's very interesting."

"How so? Mosquitoes must be pretty much the same all over the world."

"Well they aren't, why else would they be buying these sleeping nets?" He pointed at me. "Don't tell me you've never been attacked by mosquitoes when you were out in the middle of the day, jump shooting ducks in a slough. If theirs only bite at night, we'd have no problem over here. In summer, by the time it's dark at say, 9:00 or 10:00, most of us are in bed with the doors and windows shut. In winter, when it's dark by 5:30, it's too cold for the little buggers."

"So you think we should have their mosquitoes over here to replace ours?" Perley asked.

"It's the genetics of the thing, Perley," Purvis replied. "Nobody goes out at night much, so there's nobody they can bite. Then they starve to death."

"I think, Purvis," Harry Charles said, "you should cut the cheque to Belinda and congratulate her for the good work she's doing. But I don't think that, with all that effort she's putting into this charity, she'd have time to digest and appreciate your scientific thesis."

Sunny and Share

"I thought Bono was dead," Purvis said by way of greeting when I slid into my chair. "Didn't he get killed in some wilderness accident back a few years ago?"

"Well, actually it was a skiing accident and yes, he's still dead because when I was in Palm Springs they had some sort of public recognition event for him, and his widow was there."

"She's had a pretty good run since they used to be on television together, hasn't she. Done a lot of movies, more television and stuff. She must be a millionaire in her own right."

"Well, actually, Purvis, I'm afraid Sonny and Cher divorced a long time ago. The woman at this event in Palm Spring was his latest widow, I mean his widow, because Cher would be his ex-wife." I waved at Hazel, which was unnecessary because she was already on her way with my carafe and glass. "Come to think of it, though, maybe Cher could be his ex-widow while the other one would be his present widow."

Hazel put the instruments on the table in front of me and asked if the other guys were coming and if she should get their mugs on the table now so they wouldn't have to wave and wait. Purvis and I thought that made sense from an efficiency perspective and told her yes.

"Anyway, what's all this about Sonny and Cher?" I asked.

"Well, I read in the Sun that Bono was over there in Germany badgering Stephen about aid to Africa and sharing more of our wealth along with somebody called Geldof who I think is a New York guy who sings folk songs, or write books, or something."

"No, that's not Sonny, although I think the guy you're talking about maybe sounds like him. I can't say because I've never heard

And God Created Manyberries

him sing. But he does front some sort of band from over there. Anyway, he pronounces it Bono, like Mono in mononucleosis."

"Geez, you never use one word when six or seven great big ones will use up the air, do you?"

"Well, you sort of caught me off guard and I haven't even taken my first sip and I'm still coming down from a busy day. Give me time to settle in and I'll come up with something simpler, like monocular."

"That sort of dishonours Sonny though, doesn't it? If the guy is going to use his last name why doesn't he pronounce it the way Sonny did?"

"Well, I think he's Irish and if he is, they are sort of an independent bunch."

"So what made your day so busy? From what I've seen you spend most of your days sitting in the sun reading or putting golf balls on that old carpet in your backyard."

"I counted all the flowers on my tomato plants. Germinating them in January gave them a big head start and it looks like I'm going to be the tomato king of Manyberries."

"So what business is it of a guy from Ireland who you claim is a singer what Stephen does with our money?"

"Could be that he's using Sonny as a role model because Sonny was Mayor of Palm Springs and then he was either a Congressman or a Senator down there."

"Or maybe he's just another one of those radical busybodies."

Perley and Harry Charles arrived and joined us at the table. Purvis informed them that, keeping to tradition, because he arrived first the topic tonight was going to be about a guy called Bono pestering Stephen about aid to Africa. He pronounced it the way Sonny did.

"Well, I think Irene said she was going to put supper on early tonight so I can't hang around very long," Harry Charles said.

"I was thinking I might deliver a few more pieces of mail before supper," Perley shook his head in regret as he reached for his mug.

"Of course, Irene could put it in the oven if you were to talk about how the media give Paris Hilton as much coverage as Stephen and how even CBC thinks she warrants a mention."

"Or how the newspapers put her on the front page or how CTV trots after her like she was their boss at the television station." Perley was leaning toward being persuaded to finish his deliveries the next day.

"We could blend that in with all the reporting they're doing on that skinny little Lindsay Lohan and I could have my supper for breakfast," Harry Charles offered.

"Have to admit," I said, "I admire Bono for the work he's doing.

The guy's relentless and using everything he has to focus attention on the misery in Africa. Hell, they just let him move in as guest co-editor of Vanity Fair."

"What's Vanity Fair?" Perley asked.

"It's a damn good American magazine," Harry Charles answered for me. I always drop my copies off for him when I finish with them. I buy them on my periodic visits to Medicine Hat.

"By the way," he said to me, "I think we need more guys like Bono in politics. He certainly wouldn't be in it for the money or the fame. A guy like that might be just the ticket to getting young people all over the world taking an interest in politics and getting out and voting."

"Why the hell would you germinate your tomato seeds in January?" Purvis turned to me. "You shouldn't do that until May 1st."

"Well, I wanted to see if I could get tomatoes by the end of June. And it looks like I will."

"Will that be from the plants you started yourself or the ones you bought up in Calgary?" Harry Charles is my gardening guru and knows all my secrets.

"Both. Well, the plants I bought will deliver red ones and the other ones should at least be ready for frying green."

"You'll remember the old hunters' rule, I hope." Perley said. "We share what we harvest and a fried green tomato in June makes my mouth water."

"Are you still going to put a mirror behind every plant to double the sunshine they get?" Harry Charles asked.

"I still think he should pronounce it Bono, the way Sonny did," Purvis grumbled.

War Games

Perley waved an urgent hello with a rolled up dog-eared newspaper when I walked in for our daily political summit and weather debrief and paused while my eyes adjusted to the dark. "How dumb are those reporters in Ottawa?" he asked as I sat, shifted to find the spot where chair bottom and bones don't collide, and waved at Hazel to let her know she could start anytime. I am if nothing else a multi-tasker, but only at the Ranchmen's when it's cocktail hour.

"I don't know, probably not a whole lot more than the average population. Why, what did they do now?"

"They're complaining that when Stephen visited the front in Afghanistan that the whole busload of them had to stay behind and only a photographer was allowed to go with him."

"Well, they bitch and whine and snivel about everything. The worst is yet to come. Wait until the humidity blanket gets tossed over Ottawa and they'll be even crankier."

"Maybe, but this is flat-out stupid, complaining that a whole bus or plane load of them couldn't go up near the front where the troops are still engaged. Maybe they've got a death wish."

"I doubt that very much. On the other hand, considering what life is like in that Ottawa humidity, you could be on to something."

Harry Charles and Purvis joined us and Purvis asked what the topic for the night was. Perley informed him that it was the dumbness of reporters in Ottawa.

"Geez, we'll be here till closing time," Harry Charles said and waved six fingers at Hazel, to save Purvis the discomfort of lifting a stiff shoulder.

"Maybe they're not dumb, maybe they just don't know what war is about," Perley said, "but you guys know what I'm talking about."

Purvis and Harry Charles nodded but I had to fess ignorance.

"When we were over there for War Two," he said, "there was no way we would have let a bunch of non-combatants up near the front. We were there to fight and trying hard not to get ourselves killed."

"Yeah, but you had guys like Stursberg and Lynch with the troops in the middle of the action. From what those guys told me, they did their job and you did yours and it all worked out pretty well."

"Those guys travelled with us, they didn't come in crowds on foot or in buses or on airplanes. Cripes, I wouldn't be here if it had been any different."

Perley took a swallow and shook his head. "I don't know what it's like in Afghanistan but I bet our people over there keep their heads down and try to stay as invisible as we did back then."

"I guess it would be hard in any war to be inconspicuous with a flock of sheep running around in your midst, whether it's in Europe or Afghanistan." Harry Charles is like a lot of other civilians: he thinks the media often get in the way of a good news story.

"Right. The way I figure it, there's probably some enemy spotter hiding in every low spot or outhouse within firing range of where our people are. What do you think those guys are going to do if they spot a busload of people coming up to where our trenches are? They're going to lay everything they've got on that place."

"Geez, can you imagine what the media would do if some of them got taken out by a sniper? They'd be blaming Stephen for having arranged it." Purvis is not on a first name basis with Stephen – not many folks in Manyberries are – but Stephen's our guy so we dispense with the formalities.

"You know, Perley, I think you should write a letter to the editor," Harry Charles said. "I think you should say that after much discussion and contemplation, Prime Minister Harper, because of his affection for the media and respect for their important role, decided to go there unaccompanied. He wouldn't be party to anything that would put them in danger's way."

"I just might do that, if there's any newspaper that cares about what a veteran thinks and I doubt that any of them do."

"Then," Harry Charles continued, "you should write a letter to Stephen and tell him how much you respect his decision to go up there alone."

"What would that accomplish?"

"It might give him pause for thought. Next time he goes to Afghanistan, he might decide to visit the front and once the media are on their way there in their brightly painted bus flying a few dozen Maple Leaf flags, change his mind and stay back at headquarters."

Drop Your Guns in Manyberries

"How many guns do you own?" Perley had his little wire spiral shirt pocket notebook on the table in between the beer mugs. I waved at Hazel and pulled my chair up, not certain that I wanted to answer his question before determining what prompted it.

"Why do you ask? Thinking about having a gun show?"

"No, we're writing a new federal policy on gun control and we need some statistics so we can put in charts and graphs like they do in Ottawa."

"Well, give me a minute to do some reflecting." I smiled my thanks to Hazel and sat back and closed my eyes to visualize my collection.

"See, I told you guys he has so many he couldn't come up with an answer right off the top," Harry Charles said.

Harry Charles was correct. He's over at my place frequently and always asks for the keys to my two vaults where I have them stored. In fact, he often brings other people over to see my collection and gives them friendly lectures on the specific reasons for each gun. For instance, the Remington three inch magnum semi-automatic 12 gauge is for geese while the Remington pump 16 gauge is for early season ducks. There's a middle-aged 30-30 Winchester that's for use in a heavily bushed spot we call the Whitetail Patch. And the list goes on, and then on some more.

"Eighteen or 20, depending on whether you include the two old muskets. Maybe 23 or 24. I'm not going home to count them so you'll have to settle for a ballpark estimate."

"He has 26 different rifles and shotguns," Harry Charles said, "including a priceless L.C. Smith 16 gauge with two sets of barrels in a very old leather case. I've counted them."

"You've got an L.C. Smith? Cripes, you could have retired years ago if you'd sold it." Purvis has a vast knowledge of the value of just about everything.

"It was passed down from my grandfather to my father and on to me," I said, "and it only comes out one day every season."

"That would be a good argument for my plan," Purvis told Harry Charles and Perley. "Of course he'd have to pay a little extra."

"Look, I don't want to intrude here, but would you guys mind telling me the direction you're headed so I can decide whether or not to join you?"

"You know how much the gun registry in Ottawa has cost so far?" Purvis asked. "Three billion, at least. That's a lot of money and they say on the news it's only going to increase."

"Actually, the cost is around $1 billion and some estimates say the cost out into the future could hit $2 billion," I told them.

"But I've got a way for Purvis to make it hit $3 billion, Perley said, "and we'll be able to show it on the charts and graphs."

"The way Purvis figures it, charts and graphs don't lie or the politicians and bureaucrats wouldn't use them." Harry Charles and Perley had no doubt been encouraging Purvis to pursue his idea.

"So, if you have 26 rifles and shotguns to be registered we'll take that as an average and multiply it by the total population and multiply that by $20 per gun and that'll be the total projected cost of the firearms registry spread out over the years until somebody decides to cancel it."

"I think if we built a big concrete building where all the guns in Manyberries could be stored, the government would probably give us a grant." Purvis goes crazy every time he hears on the radio that somebody or some group got another grant from Ottawa. "We wouldn't bother writing down serial numbers or crap like that because everybody here knows what his or her guns are so it'd be a waste of time."

"So whenever somebody wants to go hunting or shooting at tin cans, they'd call Purvis, who'd come over with the keys. The charge would be one dollar per opening from the owner and five dollars to Ottawa for administration." Perley explained the plan with what sounded like enthusiasm.

"I think your arithmetic might be questioned," I cautioned. "Whatever the total population is, I'm certain you can't include Wendy Cukier."

"Who's she?" Purvis asked.

"She heads up some group that wants all guns registered and preferably destroyed."

"Okay, one less out of 30-some-odd million isn't going to make much of a difference in our totals." When Purvis starts chewing on an idea he's kind of like a Weimaraner on a soup bone.

"But here's the corker," Harry Charles told me. "Purvis is going to run a rental business on the side."

"I'm not certain that would work. If anybody wanted to use one of my guns, except the L.C. Smith, I'd lend it to him or her."

"I'm talking about Americans coming up here to hunt. The other part of the plan is a law that says they can't bring their guns across the border. So we advertise that Manyberries has a gun rental service and they have to come here to rent one before they go on to wherever they plan to hunt."

"The way Purvis sees it," Harry Charles explained, "there are thousands of Americans who come to Canada to hunt, so this would make Manyberries their first stop. And every one would stop by here for at least one beer, so the Ranchmen's would benefit."

"I'd even dig up my guns and put them in the rental centre," Purvis said. When they started talking about gun control back during Pierre Trudeau's time, Purvis wrapped his guns in greased canvas and buried them in his backyard. He got the idea from a retired judge in Toronto who did the same thing. From what I've heard, a lot of guns in cities and towns went underground at that time.

"And this would save us the time spent trying to find a magnifying glass to read the serial numbers and write them down to send to Ottawa." Harry Charles is less tight with his money than with his time. As he says, when you reach the age these guys have, you don't waste time waiting for bananas to ripen.

"What have you got in the way of statistics on the crime rate in Manyberries?" I asked. "Wendy Cukier uses statistics to her advantage whenever criminals in Toronto shoot one another."

"We don't have a crime rate in Manyberries. Haven't had since back when those guys tried to rob the bank in the 20s. And now that the bank's gone, we're not likely to ever have one." Purvis paused to think about something and added that maybe one or two guns could be kept in some homes in case one of the banks ever decided to open a branch again in Manyberries.

"Well, guys, there's no doubt this could be just the sort of environmentally friendly industry we need here, but there's a bit of a hitch. Stockwell has already declared a moratorium on the long gun registry while they rethink the whole registration boondoggle. Chances are nobody's going to register, if they haven't already, until they can read the signals from Ottawa."

Drop Your Guns in Manyberries

"We told Purvis that and he thinks this concrete gun bunker is still the answer." Harry Charles sat back and Purvis leaned forward.

"We'll just tell Stephen and Stockwell to cancel the whole gun registration program. They can keep the handgun part of it if they want. All the guns will be safely stored in our warehouse and whoever is in charge will make sure that no criminals can come in and borrow or rent one. In about a year, we'll start selling franchises across the country. I'll bet that would get every one of those Toronto bank guys thinking about opening a branch here."

"What about the people who've already registered? Most of them probably went out and bought vaults like they were told to by Ottawa. I don't think you can count on them as potential customers."

"I bet about 99 percent of the gun owners haven't registered so if we only get half of them, we're sitting on a gold mine. I'll bet even my judge friend in Toronto would dig his up out of the backyard. Hell, he's retired, he might even want to buy a franchise."

"Well, the bad news is I won't be a customer. Mine are all registered and I've got two sturdy vaults."

"You registered your guns? You actually sent those guys in Ottawa a cheque and told them about every one of your guns?" Purvis was astounded that I would do something so unManyberrian.

"Well, I was in a delicate position when I was in Ottawa or at least I thought I might be, so I decided to go with the law. In hindsight, it was a waste of money and – more important – time, and I'm not even as old as you guys."

"I've got a feeling if this gets around town, they might do a fundraiser to send you back," Harry Charles said, "but if you want to pay for the next round, your dark and dirty little secret might be safe with us."

"Geez, you've really screwed up the statistics I was compiling for Purvis' charts and graphs," Perley said. "Now I'm going to have to go back and do it all over again and this longhand arithmetic uses up a lot of time."

"Doesn't matter," Purvis said sternly. "We'll just consider this a freak of nature. He's part of that one percent we were never going to get anyway."

"Yeah, but 26 guns times 33 million Canadians minus this Wendy Cukier will sure bring the numbers down." Perley shook his head and bent over his notebook and began jotting down figures.

"Okay, we'll back off a little on the plan. Instead of a concrete building, we'll rent Old Rutherford's garden shed and put a lock on it."

Wooing Prince Harry

"Looks like Prince Harry got himself into a bit of stew in a bar up in Calgary the other night," Perley told me as he settled into his chair and signalled Hazel. "Seems he went in for a drink and got fastened to some young thing who then turned around and got herself plastered all over the English newspapers."

"Yeah, I heard about it on the radio," I replied. "I guess if you're Prince Harry, you're not just an ordinary soldier out for a few drinks on leave. I gather the Brit newspapers were wildly indignant about a young guy doing what young guys have always done. Those journalists are the worst hypocrites on the planet."

"Why do you say that? I thought you liked those people. You used to be one of them."

"Well, I don't dislike them, it's just that apart from teetotallers, there aren't too many reporters, just like young guys, who don't go into bars and get swacked once in a while and leer at the waitresses and maybe even make a move on them."

"And then they criticize Prince Harry for doing the same? Yeah, guess you could call that hypocrisy."

Purvis and Harry Charles joined us and Purvis was so eager to talk about something he almost forgot to wave at Hazel.

"Did you guys hear about Prince Harry?"

"We were just talking about it," Perley told him, "but I'm not sure it's got enough weight to carry us through until we leave."

"That's because you're not looking at the big picture. I was just telling Harry Charles there's a great opportunity here for Manyberries and the Ranchmen's."

"I hope you're not going to ask Hazel to start wearing what those barmaids who work at Cowboys up in Calgary wear," I said. "I don't think Manyberries is ready for that, or ever will be."

"No, what we should do is invite Prince Harry and his regiment to come down here instead of going to Calgary when they get leave. Geez, can you imagine what a whole regiment would mean to sales here? It'd put Manyberries on the maps of the world."

"I wouldn't bet on the Ranchmen's making big profits even with a regiment in residence," I said. "Because we'd be swamped by reporters coming here to report on what Harry's up to and running up huge tabs at the bar."

"What's wrong with that? Bigger sales at the bar, publicity for Manyberries, we could make him an honorary citizen and maybe the Queen would write us a letter we could hang on the wall."

"Why not make the whole regiment honorary citizens," Perley suggested. "I've got a drawer full of keys with no locks. We could say they're the keys to Manyberries and run off some sort of diploma thing on the Gestetner."

"To answer your question, Purvis, profits would suffer because those journalists have a habit of leaving town and forgetting to pay their bar tabs. And they could out-drink a regiment."

"Well, Hazel would just put up a sign saying cash up front for all drinks."

"That would be an insult to all the regulars who'd think she suddenly doesn't trust them."

"Well, I'll think about that but the general idea is a good one. They're training up at Suffield, right? How far is Suffield from here?" He turned to Harry Charles for the answer.

"Not more than a couple of hours. I think you should go on up there to extend an invitation on behalf of Manyberries, Purvis. Tell the Prince we'll make room for him at our table."

"I bet this would make history just like the Prince of Wales did when he came to Alberta and bought a ranch." Purvis paused and his eyes lit up even more. "I've got a quarter section of poor pasture that's so rocky it can't be tilled. Maybe the Prince might be interested in buying a ranch in the colony like his great uncle or whatever he was did."

"This is turning out to be a win-win-win proposition for everybody," Harry Charles observed, rather dryly. "Manyberries wins, the Ranchmen's wins, you win, Purvis, and the Prince wins because he gets to discover the real Alberta. I guess that's four wins, not three."

"I never thought about that. If I invite him I'll tell him he should come here to discover the real Alberta, still very much like the one that other Prince discovered when he bought that ranch up near Calgary."

"You're forgetting one thing, Purvis, and that's how these young

And God Created Manyberries

guys think when they're planning a night out." I paused and thought about when I used to make plans to hit a few bars. "Young guys look for bars where the waitresses are near their own age and wear outfits that reveal their personalities. They also look for joints where there are female customers who fit the same description."

"Maybe some of those waitresses might like to come and work here. I hear rents in Calgary are pretty high."

"Doubt it, Purvis. The tips they get from those high-rollers up there would probably cover the rent and then some. They get even bigger tips from guys who pretend they're high-rollers."

"Well, maybe I should just settle for selling him that quarter section and forget about making Manyberries and the Ranchmen's wealthy. It seemed like a good idea at the time."

"Look at it this way, Purvis," Harry Charles said. "Manyberries and the Ranchmen's have always gotten along just fine without any princes or potentates or even very many politicians and we always will. And don't forget, we'll always have Hazel."

Until the Cows Come Home

"Purvis has an idea he's going to put to Stephen in a letter," Perley said as I settled in and waited for Hazel to acknowledge my signal. "He thinks he's found a way for Stephen to win all the seats he needs in Ontario, Quebec and the Maritimes."

"Geez, if he has found the key, Stephen might find a vacancy on the Supreme Court for him. I can just picture Purvis in robes banging his gavel and calling for public flogging."

"He was thinking more along the lines of the Senate. Or a guaranteed nomination when Monte Solberg retires."

"The guaranteed nomination is the more likely reward." I smiled my thanks to Hazel and told her she was looking particularly radiant. She just snorted and grabbed up Perley's empty mugs. "Monte's in his oh, mid-40s, and if he decided to retire in say, 10 years, and I hope he doesn't, Purvis would be about, what, 104?"

"I think in the end he'd settle for a letter of thanks from the Prime Minister that he could get framed to hang on the wall here."

"Well, give me the executive summary before he arrives because I'm not ready for the full report with the charts and graphs."

"He's going to suggest they paint all the milk cows in all those provinces."

"What, like the maple leaf on every cow? It'll be tough to get it all done by July 1st. But no doubt it'll fire up the patriotism of the farmers if they're being paid rent for the space."

"No, he's thinking more along the lines of the Conservative logo, like they did with that stock car."

"What stock car? Did I miss something?"

"A better question is did you ever not miss something? You must be the only person in Manyberries who's oblivious to everything that happens outside the town limits."

"It's an art, Perley. You have to work on it every day to keep your mind free of clutter."

"Anyway, the Conservatives are paying some stock car driver for space on his car for their logo. Seems they figure the people who go to stock car races are their kind of people. Purvis thinks they should do the same with cows."

"Geez, you're not telling me they're holding cow races?"

"No, he's suggesting they put the logo on all the milk cows in pastures up and down every road people travel in summer. That'd be along the 400 and 401 in Ontario and all the main roads in Quebec and on down east."

"As free as my mind is of clutter, I'm almost certain that farmers don't have cow rallies and even more certain that if they did, it wouldn't be a tourist draw. And I'm not certain the Conservatives would want to claim that people who did go to a cow rally are their kind of people."

"No, you're missing the picture. The cows are billboards. They just stand in their pasture watching the tourists go by and the tourists look back and see the Conservative logo on every cow. Purvis says it's subliminal advertising just like those one-tenth of a second things he's convinced the Liberals used to put in the soap operas his wife watches."

"It's a helluva way to get the farm vote. Not a farmer in the country who'd turn down a subsidy like that."

"I think the way Purvis sees it, voters are like cows. They're placid, mostly contented standing around chewing their cuds and don't object when it's milking time."

"Man, this is about as subliminal as it gets," I said. "Do you want me to wave to Hazel for you too?" He nodded and I held up a hand and pointed down at myself and then over at him. We do that for each other in the Ranchmen's – helping friends is a tradition in our close knit community.

"You should have stayed a little longer last night when the bulb went on over Purvis' head. Harry Charles and I told him it was the best idea he'd had in a long time. When we left he said he was going to start work on his letter to Stephen when he got home. He'll probably have it finished in a week or two because drawing the cows will take some time."

"That thing about voters being like cows doesn't sound very much like Purvis."

"No, that was Harry Charles' idea. He told Purvis to work that into his letter to Stephen, and Purvis said it sounded pretty psychological so he would."

"So the thesis is people who look at cows are Conservative-minded people: honest, hard-working, tax-paying, family-loving backyard-barbecue folks? They like cows but they'll grill and eat them if it makes the family happy?"

"You should have been here last night. Purvis would have wanted to work that into his letter too." Perley took a swallow from his mug and wiped the foam off his upper lip.

"The more I think about it, the more I think Purvis has stumbled on to something. Cows give us milk and most voters think of milk and mother so they'll see the cows and think of being swaddled and safe in mommy's arms. Then when they go to vote they'll flash back to that logo and feel all warm and snugly and vote for the name with that logo attached."

"I'm left breathless by the brilliance of it all," I said and waved at Hazel to bring more tools to the table.

Atlantic Accurseds

"What do you know about this Atlantic Accord stuff?" Perley asked when I'd finished squirming around to find my grooves in the chair seat.

"Just a little less than absolutely nothing. Because I figured if I had to, I'd just ask Harry Charles."

"Well, I can't figure out why Danny Williams over in Newfoundland and Rodney MacDonald down in Nova Scotia are whining and moaning about it, or what it all means."

"It's about them wanting more provincial welfare," Purvis said. "Which means more money pouring out of Manyberries if they get their way."

I thanked Hazel for bringing me the tools and shook my head at Purvis. "They call it equalization, Purvis, not welfare. It goes back almost as far you guys and if you need any more information you'll have to ask somebody else."

"It's welfare," Purvis argued. "When did Ottawa ever send us anything but our Canada Pension Plan and Old Age Security cheques? And they claw a hell of a lot of that last one back from me to send over to Saskatchewan or down east."

"As I recall, equalization was to guarantee that all Canadians would have about the same government services and standard of living."

"Exactly. That's my point. It's welfare." Purvis thumped his empty mug on the table hard enough to signal Hazel.

"But as I understand it, the money from oil and gas is pouring into those provinces just like it does into Edmonton and those guys want that plus all the money they've been getting from Ottawa to boot." Perley is not as emphatic in his opinions as Purvis until he gathers some knowledge on the issue.

"Well, I've been pretty busy and haven't had time to read any newspapers if anybody from up north left any behind. That's probably your best source for what it's all about because it sure as hell isn't me." No matter how hard they tried, they weren't going to draw me into an argument on this particular subject.

"They're emptier than you are," Perley snorted. "I was up in Medicine Hat yesterday and bought three newspapers and came home and watched the news on television and still don't know what the fuss is all about."

"What's been keeping you busy?" Purvis asked. "Looking for golf balls you drove off that rug on to the prairie?"

"No, I was estimating the number of pounds of tomatoes I'll get from all of my plants. I multiplied the flowers by the average weight of the varieties I planted."

"There wasn't one thing in the newspapers or on television to tell me how much those provinces have been getting from Ottawa, how much they're getting in royalties or what they'll get in the future. I wasted my money buying those papers and that satellite dish."

"Well, how can you expect the media to explain something they don't understand themselves, or won't take the time to understand?" I asked.

"If you get more tomatoes than you need, the wife and I'll be glad to take some off your hands," Purvis said. He's a very generous guy in that regard.

"How in the name of blazes do those media people expect me to make up my mind on this if they don't give me the details? They tell me that Danny Williams says one thing and Stephen Harper says they might take it to court. I still don't know what they're arguing about."

Harry Charles settled into his chair as Perley concluded his lament. "Surely you wouldn't expect the media to give you charts and details regarding equalization and transfer payments when they need that space for Paris Hilton's daily jail journal?"

"Well, I'd like them to give me enough information so that if I wrote a letter to Stephen or Monte Solberg about it I'd know whose side I was on."

"You know they've probably got billions of barrels of oil out there under the ocean," Harry Charles told us, "and already Newfoundland has collected a billion dollars in royalties. And they've been getting all that money from Ottawa for equalization at the same time. Danny Williams wants Ottawa to keep sending that money while he keeps collecting billions in royalties. The way equalization works, once a province gets as rich as Alberta or Ontario, they start cutting back on what they get from Ottawa."

"Sounds fair to me," Purvis said, looking around the Ranchmen's to see if there were any easier political debates he could join.

"Are you telling me that, wait a minute, are you saying that, hold on," Perley was confused. "Are you saying that Danny Williams wants his province to be treated as poor so it keeps getting that money from Ottawa even though the money he makes from oil is more than what he gets from Ottawa?"

Harry Charles was smiling. "A bit confusing, wouldn't you say?"

"So this is like a guy who's on welfare and gets a job and sues the government so he can keep getting welfare cheques while he's collecting paycheques from the job?" Purvis was back in the conversation.

"I guess if you boiled it right down, that's what you'd get at the bottom of the pot," Harry Charles said.

"See, I told you it was welfare," Purvis said and he turned to me. "When you give us those tomatoes, the wife will boil them down and then toss in some of that venison sausage you gave me and we use that over spaghetti in the winter. If you give us enough and she makes us enough, I might be able to slip you a jar."

The National Press Club of Manyberries

"I read that your old Ottawa watering hole has gone dry, bankrupt, and kaput," Harry Charles said to me as he settled into his chair. "I guess the drop in revenue when you left sealed its envelope."

"Well, it was a long time coming. Probably just as well I left Ottawa now there's no place to go at the end of the day, or weekends, or noon when Parliament isn't sitting." Despite having operated for 79 years, the National Press Club of Canada in Ottawa had declared bankruptcy and slammed the doors. I had been tracking its demise since leaving Ottawa so wasn't surprised when they made it official.

"We could have one night where we hold a vigil to mark its passing," Perley said. "You can wear your National Press Club golf shirt if we ban cameras so you won't be embarrassed."

"Well, some sort of ceremony might be appropriate, like one moment of silence and one glass of wine. Not that I don't think it's a shame that a so-called "national capital" doesn't have a press club. I don't know about the golf shirt part unless I can find some sort of stretching rack."

"The newspaper said it started up back in 1928 so it had a pretty good run," Harry Charles said. "That's not as old as the Ranchmen's but still, for a place like Ottawa, not bad in terms of longevity."

"Yeah, I joined the first time in late 1964 or early '65 and maintained membership off and on ever since."

"If it would make you feel any better, we could declare the Ranchmen's the new National Press Club of Canada," Perley said. "It'd just be among us here at the table so as not to get everybody riled up thinking we're going to have some sort of connection with Ottawa, or that we'd want to."

"What did they do at the Press Club, apart from drink?" Purvis asked. "I mean if that's all they did, they'd fit right in here if they wanted to visit."

"Well, they had an annual golf tournament, a Mother's Day event, Newsmakers' Breakfasts, billiards tournaments, and uh, well, the odd time, a shuffleboard tournament." I paused. "Oh yeah, pretend horse races on the bar, Canada and Remembrance Day events, and um, we once had a chilli cook-off between Members of Parliament."

"Whew!" Harry Charles stifled a pretend yawn. "Leaves you breathless, just thinking about all the excitement and glitter."

"Maybe we could declare this table the National Press Club of Canada," Perley said, "and shorten the activities list to drinking."

"We could get a poster of Parliament and pin it to the curtain to make it official," Harry Charles suggested. "But then somebody might remember the National Energy Program and tear it down the same night."

"Well, Thor graduated from her calligraphy correspondence course. Maybe we could ask her to draw a sign we could tack to the wall behind me. She could write that This Table is The National Press Club of Canada". Purvis too was showing sympathy for the loss of a fine old Ottawa institution.

"I don't think you should go too big to start," I said. "Get some kid with a wood burning set to create a discrete little table plaque with National Press Club of Canada burned into it. Then, whenever Harry Charles is pulling together his column for the Bald Prairie Tattler, we'll set the plaque out and sit around discussing what Harry Charles plans to write."

"I don't want the help or advice of a committee. I don't need a bunch of second-guessers sitting around or looking over my shoulder. But I wouldn't mind setting out the plaque after everybody's read the column and wants to congratulate me on it."

"Well, that would certainly be in keeping with the tradition of the media portion of the membership," I told him. "At least where they look for congratulations on the fine work they do."

"I think we should try to make this as much like the real thing as we can," Perley commented. "You said they have shuffleboard tournaments?"

"Well, not for a few years, but they did have them at one time. I think the last one might have been in about, oh, 2004."

"Well, we've got shuffleboard here. What we can do is sit around and drink and when somebody plays shuffleboard we'll drink some more and watch them play."

"Geez, guys I'm getting a lump in my throat. Just imagining what Perley's suggesting makes me feel like I'm in the Club right now."

Goodbye Charlie

Charlie was probably the best dog any family ever had the good fortune to know. He came to our house in the autumn of 1973 on Grey Cup Day, also known as Grand National Drunk Day. I had already picked him out of the litter and had to wait until he could part company with his mother and brothers and sisters.

I brought him home in the sleeve of a heavy tweed ankle-length coat. When we got into the house I let him stick his little wet nose out so our daughter could touch it. She was three at the time and had a cat called Mitt and it didn't take long until all three of them were inseparable fast friends.

Mitt was a tomcat who weighed 22 pounds (in winter when he didn't exercise much) and he didn't take any nonsense from any of the neighbourhood dogs. But he loved little Charlie. He even let Charlie eat his Purina Cat Chow when Charlie nosed into his dish. That was Charlie's first-ever hard food and he ate Purina Cat Chow for the rest of his life. In his last years, I had to pour warm water over it to soften it for him because he had lost some molars due to old age. He lived with us for 19 years and that made him equivalent to something like a 133-year- old person. I don't think too many of us will have all our teeth if we ever hit that age.

Jennifer played with dolls but with Charlie she had a real live one. She'd sit on the second floor landing and take the dress off one of her dolls and try to put it on Charlie. When that didn't fit, she'd haul out some of her own clothes and transform him into a girly dog. And when she walked up or down the stairs, Charlie would be right beside her so she could hang on to the loose skin on his neck and steady herself.

Charlie would go to bed with her every night and when she was

And God Created Manyberries

asleep, come into our room to jump up on our bed and burrow under the comforter. He'd spend the night there until he heard Jennifer stirring and then he'd head back to her bed so she could wake up with him.

When Michael was born, Charlie was right there, curious and probably thinking we'd brought a new plaything home for him. He split his nights by sleeping under Michael's crib and then going to sleep with Jennifer before giving us a few hours. I think he tried to give us at least three visits each per night.

As Michael grew and learned to walk, Charlie was right there beside him. Michael would grab whatever was handy on Charlie and pull himself upright and then hold on like the devil while Charlie walked around the room.

Charlie had been the runt of the litter and, like a lot of runts, human especially, compensated by being absolutely fearless. The only fear he couldn't conquer was water. He wouldn't even walk in a rain puddle on the sidewalk. Out in the country you could throw a sirloin steak in a shallow pond and he wouldn't go after it.

Sirloin steak reminds me of the time Charlie decided to be a cow dog. We were out for a Sunday drive and stopped on a rutted trail to let him have a run. He saw some cows in a field and went off to explore. The cows saw him coming and were as curious about him as he was about them. They got in a waddling jog as big Holsteins will do and Charlie stopped dead in his tracks. There were about 30 of them jog-waddling toward him when he decided retreat was in order. As he turned and started to trot away, the cows picked up speed. That put Charlie into a dead run toward the split rail fence between the road and the pasture. Instead of ducking under the lower rail Charlie dove between the lower and middle rails. It didn't work. He got stuck there for a few seconds with his head and front legs on one side and his hind legs doing a frog kick to try get traction in the air. The cows were pretty close by the time he wiggled free. He ran straight to our station wagon and got into the back where he knew he was safe and started barking at them.

An even stranger thing happened a few miles down the road when we came across a herd of cows and calves that had gotten through the fence and were on the road and in both ditches. The rear window was open and Charlie sailed through it and started barking at the cows. They got into a run and he pulled up alongside a yearling calf and jumped up and grabbed it by the brisket and hung there for at least 20 feet. His hind end was hitting the road about every two steps until he finally let loose and trotted happily back to the car.

The kids thought that had been great fun and Charlie seemed

quite proud of himself. I have often wondered if it was revenge that triggered his chase, grab and hold trick. It's pretty hard to explain to a dog, even one like Charlie, that no two cows are alike. Even if he did understand the concept he'd probably argue that if one cow deserved it, they all did.

From that day on, Charlie barked at every cow he saw. Try to imagine driving across the prairie by pastures with several hundred head of cattle with a dog that insists on barking at every one. It might be part of the reason why my hearing isn't as good as it once was.

Harry Charles loved Charlie and the three of us spent a lot of happy days either fishing or hunting. Not that Charlie fished or hunted. He liked going hunting because he could always find cow manure in which to wallow, and fishing was sort of fun if he could find a dead fish to roll on. Charlie just naturally preferred the stronger colognes.

Harry Charles watched him all the time because, as he said, "you never know what the little mutt will do next."

There was the time we were fishing a tiny brook that a man could easily jump across but that had a narrow sapling laid bank to bank. Harry Charles was fishing one side of the brook and I was on the opposite side when Charlie decided he wanted to visit HC. Of course he wouldn't set a foot in the water so he had to use the sapling as a bridge. Halfway across he took a misstep and only managed to save himself by hanging on with his front legs. He clung there but his hold was slipping and he knew it when his tail and then his bum touched the water. He appeared to be trying to chin himself on the sapling and was probably unappreciative of the fact that Harry Charles was laughing as loud at Charlie's predicament as I ever heard him laugh. Finally his forepaws just couldn't hang on and he slipped rear first into the brook. It wasn't more than eight inches deep so Charlie didn't even have to swim. He just clambered up the bank and stood there shaking off the water and shivering a little from fear.

Harry Charles was still laughing. "Geez, I've never seen a dog chin himself like Charlie just did. And when he lifted his hind end up so he almost jackknifed I was wishing I'd had a movie camera."

What Charlie had done to himself was scramble up out of the creek on the bank opposite from the car and me. Harry Charles took a short skip and hop across when it was time for lunch and that left Charlie all alone on that side.

He ran for several hundred yards in both directions but couldn't find a way to get across. Harry Charles walked to the sapling and

And God Created Manyberries

tried to coax Charlie to cross on it but there was no way he was going to risk that trip again.

Finally, Harry Charles waded across and picked up Charlie and waded back so he could join us for lunch. He surely loved that little dog.

That was why, when it was time for Charlie to go to sleep for the last time, I asked Harry Charles if he would please go to the veterinarian with me and Charlie.

It was something we all had been dreading and I told Harry Charles I wasn't sure I could do it alone or even with somebody along to steady me.

"You owe it to Charlie to be there with him at the end," he said. "He's given you all of himself for all these 19 years and you have to be there with him so he can go to rest assured that nothing is wrong and that he's just getting sleepy."

"Geez, I just don't know if I can do it without breaking down," I said. "I don't want to wind up in front of people crying like a baby."

"Tell you what," Harry Charles said, "I'll go with you and Charlie and even though he doesn't seem to know what's going on, maybe he'll think we're going off hunting or fishing or looking for something wicked to roll in."

So we went to the veterinarian and I held Charlie and told him we were going hunting and to a place where there's always bad stuff to roll in and that he could have all the cat chow he could eat and that Mitt would be there and that we all loved him. And the vet gave him the needle and he dozed off with me holding him and Harry Charles holding me.

When Charlie was sound asleep the vet ushered us out the back door. I guess he didn't want the humans and his other patients in the waiting room seeing two grown men crying.

Racing a Pheasant

Autumn on the prairies, for some of us, is the best season of the year. Even though it signals that winter is approaching and bringing with it the year end, it's a season of anticipation and joy. There are still plenty of days left for those of us who golf and all three months before December are ideal for hunting. And, if you're not doing either of those, you can still go fishing. There's no other time of the year when you can, legally or logically, do all three. Weather permitting, and most years it does, you can play 18 holes of golf in the morning, hunt birds in the afternoon and, in the evening, cast to rising trout on the river.

The best autumn we ever had offered all of that and more. In September, Harry Charles, Perley, sometimes Purvis and Four-Eyed Tom, and I had days where we hunted ducks in the morning and evening and upland birds in between. In October, we hunted geese and ducks and pheasants the rest of the day. In late October, Harry Charles and I hunted antelope out near the sand dunes and got one each. In November, we each brought home a Whitetail and a Mule Deer. Harry Charles called it the most spectacular hunting season he'd ever experienced. The freezers were jammed at all of our houses with enough game meat to last a year, at which point we would start all over again.

It was his tradition as we left each favourite spot, whether it was a hot and secret deer spot, remote slough or corn field where the geese congregated, for Harry Charles to bid it adieu and inform it that he hoped to return the following year. He would add that he hoped next year would be as good as this one and that we'd be welcome. He stood outside the Suburban and repeated his mantra in late November before we left our favourite Mule Deer spot up

And God Created Manyberries

near Drumheller and then spent the whole drive home telling me and Perley about how he'd never had, or heard of, such a wonderful season.

He was still talking about it when I walked into the Ranchmen's for his birthday, on December 21st. He had taken his Whitetail with a 12 gauge slug at 80 yards and that deer was running full tilt and he was explaining to Perley and Purvis that it was a Hail Mary shot because he'd already missed on the first one. I told them I'd never seen, or expected to see again, a shot like that and raised my glass to toast his marksmanship.

It was a grand party and folks from the other tables kept dropping by to wish him a happy birthday and offer him a drink. Some of the guys wanted to hear about his equally impressive shot when he harvested his Mule Deer at 230 yards while it was walking. Perley had witnessed that and had already told the story several times about "Dead-Eye Harry Charles" and his unbeatable skill with his old Savage 250.3000.

Late in the evening as we were walking to our respective homes, Harry Charles told me had been up to Calgary to see a doctor.

"I've been up a couple of times to see him to get some tests," he told me. "Yesterday, he told me to start getting my affairs in order."

I knew what he meant, but somehow it didn't register. It took me several more steps before I could ask him what he meant, hoping I wasn't going to hear what I'd already heard.

"The Doc told me I've got a fast-moving cancer and this will be my last Christmas and to get all the necessary legal work done. He said I've got something like 90 days, if I'm lucky. It's the pancreas."

I just kept walking and staring straight ahead into the darkness. I couldn't find any words, wasn't even sure where I was except that I was wishing it was somewhere else, hopefully a bad dream.

"One of the things I want to get in order is my freezer," he continued. "I'm asking you to clean it out because I know Irene won't go near it with all that game meat in it. Not for a long time anyway, if ever. Take what you want and give the rest to folks around town who need it." He stopped and gave his lower back a rub. "My back bothered me the whole season and I just chalked it up to getting old. Turns out it wasn't my back at all, it was this pancreas thing."

We kept on walking but I think we had slowed our pace. "The other thing I want you to look after is my guns. Make sure the right guys get the right ones, the ones they need and will use and not sell or trade."

I gave him my promise that I'd look after those things for him and asked if there was anything else.

"Yes, you can drop in on Irene as often as possible. She's going to need some friendly company for quite a while until she gets used to my having gone away."

He stopped and looked up at a cloudless sky and the millions of stars. "And remember the good times, always remember the good times, because it helps to get over the bad times."

I didn't go straight home when I left him at his gate. I went northwest out of town where the closest prairie was and took a long walk and cried like a baby.

After Harry Charles passed away, we all decided, without discussion, to make sure that his beloved Irene didn't spend any days alone. We gave her a little time to grieve and mourn but after that she had visitors every day.

Perley would drop in with the mail and Purvis and Three-Eyed Tom would drop in before they made their late afternoon saunter to the Ranchmen's. Hazel would stop by with a little silver flask and pour Irene her favourite vodka and 7-Up, no ice please and the 7-Up equal to the measure of the vodka, no more and no less. I'd visit as often as I could and I know Irene looked forward to my visits.

Harry Charles taught me just about everything I know about hunting and fishing and we did a lot of that together. We'd come back to his place after every adventure and I'd have to stay for a few drinks while we entertained Irene with tales of what we did and what mischief there might have been. Harry Charles was such a terrific storyteller that she'd be laughing in no time as he recounted our antics, some of them true and some not quite true.

Anyway, after he passed away, whenever I visited she would ask me if I remembered some time or other when we were hunting and she'd say Harry Charles surely loved that particular day.

One time she asked me if I remembered the time Charlie got into a race with a cock pheasant. She told me Harry Charles would pull that one out of his memory, even in his last weeks, and retell it to her and was still able to laugh about it.

What Irene was trying to do was prompt me to tell a story she'd heard a hundred times but because it had Harry Charles in it, she wanted to hear it again. He had been her whole life for 60 years and he was still her whole life and would be again when she finally went to join him. If a story had Harry Charles in it, Irene was content to let you tell it while she closed her eyes and imagined what he was doing, how he was laughing or standing there with his old Ithaca 12 gauge over his shoulder and just grinning.

I'd change the story title from time to time. Sometimes it was Charlie in a race with a cock pheasant and other times it was Charlie's first pheasant. It didn't matter as long as it had Harry Charles in it somewhere.

We were out driving the gravel roads north of Manyberries looking for pheasants or Hungarian partridge and had been stopping at and walking every likely spot we saw. Charlie was with us but Charlie didn't go hunting just to go hunting. He went hunting to find cow manure to roll in or to bark at cows and fence posts while we were driving.

It was getting about that time when we had to start angling south to get back down to Manyberries before dark when we spotted the pheasant in the middle of the road several hundred yards ahead.

"There's our fourth for the day," Harry Charles said as I eased the Suburban forward, hoping the pheasant would head for the ditch and squat. But he didn't. He stayed right in the middle of the road and watched as I pulled up and stepped out of the Suburban. Harry Charles stayed put, confident that the bird was mine. I put one cartridge in my shotgun and started walking toward the bird, forgetting to close the door.

Charlie, thinking there might be some cow manure around, hopped out and followed me until he spotted the pheasant. He took a little run at it and the bird ran and then flew. I fired once and the bird folded in the air and came down, apparently dead, in the wheat stubble in the adjacent field.

Charlie, who'd never shown any sign of interest in hunting, trotted across the ditch, ducked under the barbed wire, and headed for the dead bird. I watched and waited, hoping he might even fetch it back, although doubting it very much.

When he got close enough to almost sniff the pheasant, it stood up and looked at him and he fell back a little. I guessed maybe one pellet had grazed the pheasant's head and knocked it out. Then the pheasant started to run and Charlie started running too.

So there was the pheasant running full tilt across the stubble and Charlie running right alongside, with his head turned looking at the pheasant as he ran.

By that time Harry Charles was out of the Suburban and standing beside me watching and waiting to see what Charlie would do. I had only put one cartridge in the shotgun and couldn't have fired a shot anyway because Charlie was too close, almost shoulder to shoulder with that pheasant.

"It looks like Charlie's having a race with that bird," said Harry Charles. "Because if he was going to grab it and fetch it back to us, he would have done it by now. Besides, it looks he's having fun racing the damn thing."

When they were about 150 yards out in the field the pheasant jumped and flew and made a banking turn to come back at us.

Harry Charles had left his shotgun in the Suburban and I had fired the only shell I had and there wasn't time to go back and get another so I could shoot the pheasant on the wing as it soared overhead.

But I didn't need another cartridge. The pheasant flew directly over our heads and slammed head first into a poplar tree and broke its neck. At least we figured it broke its neck. It might have suffered fatal skull damage. We didn't do an autopsy.

Charlie meanwhile was racing back and watching the bird as it gained distance from him. He was watching too closely because he hit the lower strand of barbed wire right at throat level.

Harry Charles walked over to where the bird was and picked it up, mostly to save Charlie from feeling squeamish about picking up the first bird he ever killed.

Charlie was making what sounded like acking sounds because of the barbed wire hitting him in the throat. He went back and climbed into the Suburban, still acking.

Harry Charles barely made it up out of the ditch before he doubled over laughing. He had tears in his eyes when he caught his breath.

"Geez, I've never seen anything like that in my life," he said. "There's Charlie running and enjoying a race with a cock pheasant. Then the damn bird takes flight and goes right over our heads and slams into a poplar tree and there isn't another stand of poplars for 10 miles in any direction."

"Do we record this as Charlie's kill?" I wondered and that started Harry Charles laughing again.

So I retold that story to Irene and her eyes just shone as she imagined Harry Charles doubled over laughing at the antics of his friend Charlie. "He used to call it the time Charlie ran a pheasant to death in a foot race," she said. "Other times he said it was the time Charlie herded a cock pheasant into a poplar tree because he wasn't carrying a gun."

She sipped her vodka and 7-Up and closed her eyes for a few moments. "I'll bet wherever they are right now, Harry Charles and Charlie are in a field, with one of them looking for cow manure to roll in and the other one for birds for supper. They make a good pair up there," she said.

The Lone Prairie

West and south of Manyberries there is a single grave that we often drive by when we're hunting. There's only the one grave and the few people I've asked about it say they don't know who was buried there. We have driven by it at least once every autumn and sometimes twice if we return on the same road after a hunting excursion.

Every autumn Harry Charles insisted on stopping and tending to the grave. He'd wipe the dust off and pick a few colourful weeds and put them by the headstone.

He said it was something a gang of hunters he knew in Ontario did every year. To get to their cabin they travelled by boat up a river that drains into the upper reaches of Georgian Bay. There were a couple of old lumber shanties on the river that spoke of earlier times when the loggers spent whole winters felling the big stands of old growth trees that had grown there since before the Europeans first set foot on North American shores.

Halfway up the river on the east bank there was an old cross that somebody spotted many years after they first started going there. Somehow on all those trips up and down that river they never saw the cross until one year it just happened to be more visible.

Harry Charles was there that year and all three boats pulled over to the shore so they could look at the cross. There was no name on the cross or note in a jar or tin can to identify the occupant or explain how he came to be buried there. But the oldest man in the crowd, who was born in 1878 and had been a logger, said it was probably another logger who drowned during the spring log drive. He said it was customary to bury the poor soul wherever they retrieved his body and to plant a cross to mark the spot. And they would nail or hang his boots from the nearest tree, even if they were good boots, because it was bad luck to wear a dead man's boots. If they could locate the man's family, they would inform them their husband or father had received a decent burial and was resting on the banks of whatever river killed him.

The next day, a few of the boys returned to the grave with a shovel, a hammer and some nails. They nailed the two pieces so they'd hold for another hundred years and planted the cross a little more deeply.

The next year they brought along a can of white paint and painted the cross. And every year after that they gave it a fresh coat. They also gave the occupant a name: they called him Emil, which the oldest man said had been a pretty popular name among French Canadian loggers.

Nobody ever discussed it or talked about it but they followed that ritual every autumn, Harry Charles said, until they were all too old to go to that camp. The last surviving one sold the lease and that ended 45 years of rousing good times in a camp that wasn't much larger than a one car garage and was lined with army bunks and decorated with calendars going back to the 1930s.

Harry Charles liked that ritual and the unspoken sentimentality of tough old coots who wanted their adopted logger to know somebody cared enough to come back every year and give his cross a fresh coat of paint.

So that became our ritual west and south of Manyberries where this lonesome grave was located. Harry Charles would ask me to pull the Suburban over or he would drive in his little Renault station wagon and get out and dust off the headstone with a hand brush he kept for sweeping the vehicle. Then he'd pick a few colourful weeds and lay them gently by the headstone.

Year after year we did that and never spoke while we were doing it, unless it was to talk about what a beautiful spot it was for anybody who loved the prairie.

Straight south of the location was a wide valley with a bit of a creek. Off to the east and west it was pretty much all flat land. Very often there were deer and antelope tracks around the grave and a few times we'd see mallards flying over, heading for the creek in the valley.

Harry Charles liked the location. He said it wouldn't be bad at all to be there for eternity if you had deer and antelope visit you from time to time and ducks flying overhead in all the seasons except winter.

I used an old line from W.C. Fields, who said on his gravestone he wanted the inscription "I'd rather be in Philadelphia".

And God Created Manyberries

Harry Charles chuckled a little at that and said yeah, he guessed if given a choice, most people would rather be any place than in a grave, maybe even in Toronto.

He had concluded that whoever our friend was, he was buried there because he loved the land, the prairie and, maybe, for some very personal reason, this particular little patch.

When Harry Charles passed away there was no quiet location like that in the country for his gravesite. He and his beloved Irene had purchased their gravesite in a regular cemetery years before with the understanding that it would be for both of them. They had vowed to spend their lives together and they did and they wanted to spend eternity together and they are.

At Harry Charles' funeral, some of the boys brought a few things for him to take along on his journey. One old friend brought along a cock pheasant's tail feather. Somebody else sprinkled a few wheat kernels on his casket as a reminder of autumn hunts in wheat fields. I arranged for his favourite jackknife to be in his pocket. We put a small bottle of black rum in there with him and a few cartridges from his favourite guns.

At the graveside the reverend was saying the last prayer when something prompted me to look skyward.

Although it was still winter there were two mallards in flight up there, giving him a flypast. One was a drake, the other a hen and they were well within shotgun range. That was when the wind made my eyes tear up a little.

The following autumn, together with another hunting buddy of Harry Charles, I went out after antelope. We harvested one each.

"That'll have Harry Charles smiling," I said. "Let's get them dressed and head back to Manyberries. We can have a quick snort of rum to celebrate and another quick one for Harry Charles."

We didn't go directly back to Manyberries and the Ranchmen's. We went west and a little south where we dusted off the lonely headstone and pulled a few colourful weeds to replace the ones Harry Charles had put there the year before.